Investigating

CW00419312

Marie Newby
Head of Home Economics, Mark Hall School, Harlow

Elaine Poole
Area Manager for Life Skills, Rainsford School, Chelmsford

Stanley Thornes (Publishers) Ltd

First published in 1990 by:
Stanley Thornes (Publishers) Ltd
Leckhampton
CHELTENHAM GL53 0DN
England

British Library Cataloguing in Publication Data

Newby, Marie
    Investigating Food
    Pupil's book
    i. Man, Nutrition
    I. Title   II. Poole, Elaine
    613.2

    ISBN 0–7487–0045–5

Typeset by Tech-Set, Gateshead, Tyne & Wear
Printed and bound in Great Britain at The Bath Press, Avon

Preface

Investigating Food is a textbook for pupils following food studies courses for GCSE Home Economics. The individual chapters in the book give information on the main topics of food study and investigations have been included throughout each chapter to encourage pupils to find out even more for themselves.

The investigations enable the pupils to practise the skills that are assessed for GCSE and the use of different investigation levels, explained below, allows the pupils to gain confidence in investigative procedures and progress to working out their own ideas for investigations.

Investigation Level 1 provides the pupils with information and guidance to allow them to collect and record relevant data.

Investigation Level 2 provides the pupils with a brief and suggests possible methods to use.

Investigation Level 3 provides the pupils with an area of study to investigate and leaves the interpretation and direction up to the individual.

All pupils are expected to start at Level 1.

There is a teacher's pack to accompany the textbook for pupils. This contains photocopiable worksheets for use with the investigations. The worksheets provide information, give details of practical and written tasks and some contain recipes. Most of them are intended as time savers as they avoid the need for pupils to copy out tables and they may store information on them to keep as a record of their investigative work.

Worksheet	Suitable points at which to refer to the worksheets are indicated by boxed items within the textbook for pupils.

Acknowledgements

The authors and publishers are grateful to the following for supplying photographs and realia and giving permission for reproduction:

Barnaby's Picture Library (p. 9)
BP, Harlow (p. 95)
The proprietor of the Crosse and Blackwell and Healthy Balance trade marks and the copyright (p. 62)
Sally and Richard Greenhill (p. 45)
Photo Co-Op (p. 26 and p. 72, top and bottom)
J Sainsbury plc (p. 80)
Claire Starkey (p. 61)
World Health Organization (p. 11)

Contents

Introduction

Home Economics is an area of study that brings together knowledge, experience and practical activities, all aimed at maintaining and improving ourselves and our personal environments.

There are four major aspects in the study of GCSE Home Economics. These are **Family**, **Food**, **Home** and **Textiles**.

This book looks closely at **Food**, but is involved in linking the four areas together by common themes.

The common themes are:

Human Development
Efficiency
Health
Safety and Protection
Values
Aesthetics
Interaction with the Environment.

As a GCSE student of **Food** you will be assessed during the course on the objectives listed below.

1   To analyse situations in the field of Home Economics by identifying the various human needs and material factors involved and to recognise the interrelationships of these needs and factors.

2   To recall, seek out, select, record and apply knowledge relevant to the needs and factors identified.

To use investigative procedures:

3   To test and compare methods, materials and equipment;

4   To observe, measure and record observations accurately and systematically;

5   To interpret evidence in its various forms as a basis for making judgements and choices;

6   To justify judgements and choices in the light of evidence;

7   To decide upon and plan a course of action which takes into account the priorities identified;

8   To carry out the planned course of action by applying the required skills;

9   To assess and evaluate the effectiveness of the course of action.

The relevant objectives are listed by number at the beginning of each chapter.

Designing your own experiments

Why experiment?

You need to experiment to find out about something or to prove something such as an idea that you have but are not definite about.

How to experiment

The method is the most important part of the experiment. It needs to be carefully planned, organised, checked and sometimes revised to make sure that it is designed to give the results you need. The method must be safe.

 Where heat, chemicals or special equipment are used, care must be taken and the experiments may need to be carried out in a laboratory (check with your teacher).

The experiment needs to be controlled. This means that one factor is deliberately changed, this is the **variable**, whilst other conditions that might affect the results are fixed, as far as possible, these are the **constants**. If there is more than one variable it is difficult to tell the cause of changes that may be noticed, and the experiment may become invalid. So **remember only one variable!**

Variables can creep in unexpectedly and it is important to be as accurate as possible when weighing, measuring, timing, labelling, carrying out a process and recording results.

Collecting and recording data

You need to decide what data is to be collected and how it is to be recorded. Data is easier to see and refer to if it is set out in a table, graph, pie chart or pictogram. Look at the example below.

Survey to find out what people eat in their packed lunches

Number of people

Tables, graphs and charts need to be given a suitable title to help others understand what information is being shown. On graphs you must always label the lines going up and along the chart — these are the axes. What title could be given to each of the examples shown here?

1   Chart to show . . . ?

EQUIPMENT USED	TIME TAKEN	VOLUME OF EGG WHITE	COST OF EQUIPMENT
Balloon whisk	2 mins	6.5 cm depth	£1.50
Rotary hand whisk	1 min 10 secs	5 cm depth	£3.00
Electric hand whisk	35 secs	3.5 cm depth	£12.00

2   Pie chart to show . . . ?

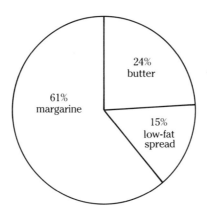

3   Graph to show . . . ?

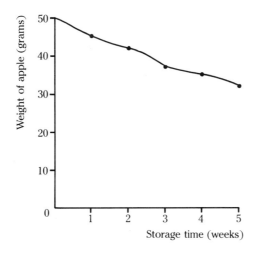

On pictograms you choose a logo (symbol) to represent each set of results. A key or code is needed to explain what each logo represents.

Remember that data should be as objective as possible. However, subjective data collected by conducting questionnaires or using sensory appraisal in taste testing also has a value.

Think about the number and cross-section of people you employ in your testing.

Drawing conclusions

Your conclusions must be taken from observations you have made and data that has been collected. You should not be tempted to add what you think the results ought to show or what you expected to find.

Remember to refer back to the initial aim, what you set out to prove or find out.

Safety in experimental work

You

- Concentrate on the task you are doing.
- Be aware of the people around you so that accidents are not caused by your actions.
- Always put a test-tube in a holder when heating in a bunsen flame.
- If chemicals are spilt on the skin, wash them off immediately with cold water and tell your teacher.

Dress

- Wear an overall or protective apron.
- Wear safety goggles when heating chemicals or any liquid using a bunsen burner.
- Long hair must be tied back.

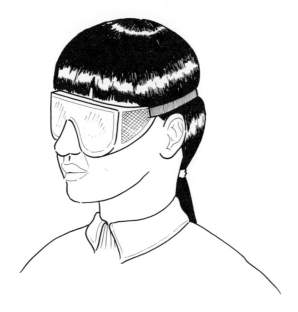

Place

- Some experiments, e.g. experiments using poisonous chemicals and experiments in micro-biology, should only be carried out in the science laboratory under teacher supervision.
- Experiments that involve food to be eaten must only be carried out in the Home Economics room or a kitchen.

Equipment

- Test tubes, beakers, etc. should be made from safety glass (e.g. Pyrex®) when heating something or using hot liquids.
- Never touch electrical equipment in use, including plugs, with wet hands.
- Always check equipment is turned off after use.
- Further information is available in the booklet: *Safety in Science Laboratories* (DES Safety Series Number 2, published by HMSO)

Investigations

Investigations have been included in this book to introduce you to this type of work and to give you an opportunity to practise and gain experience in investigating. Investigations are part of your GCSE Food coursework. The investigations in the book are classified into Levels 1, 2 and 3. You should start at Level 1, the tasks are set and you are told what methods to use. Sometimes a worksheet is available to help you record your results in a clear and organised way, your teacher will be able to give you a copy of the worksheet. The worksheets also provide additional information and further practical and theoretical investigative tasks. Suitable points at which to refer to the worksheets are given in the pupils' book. You will need this information to help you draw your own conclusions from what you have found out.

Once you are familiar with investigative work you may be able to progress to Level 2. The tasks are set and some possible methods for investigating are given, but you need to choose the most suitable method.

Investigations at Level 3 are for those who are experienced and confident in investigative work. An area of study is given but you have to write your own brief, list your aims and work out the best methods to use to achieve your aims.

All the stages involved in producing a coursework investigation are important.

Clear written evidence of ideas, planning, analysis, interpretation and evaluation are as important as the methods used and results obtained.

You must show what you know, understand and can do.

Title

Identify an area of study. Be specific, limit the area for investigation to something you can manage.

Aim

Clearly describe your aim or purpose. Remember it must be realistic and achievable.
- Analyse the task you have set yourself. List the things you already know and the things you are trying to find out.
- Put these in order of importance.
- Decide how you can obtain the information required.
- Look back at your aim. Will you be able to achieve it using these methods? Decide which method will be most suitable.

Method

State **in detail** how you **will** obtain the information required to help you achieve your aim.

Checklist

- Is it practical, in relation to resources available?
  (time, cost, materials, ingredients, equipment and access to information)
- Does it show different skills?
  (experimental and practical work, use of surveys, questionnaires or research)
- Is it going to be as accurate as possible?
- Can you do it? !!!!!

Recording results

Results must be clearly presented in an easy to follow format.

Use bar or line graphs, pictograms, pie charts, results tables, sketches, diagrams and photographs where appropriate.

Analysis or interpretation of results

Explain clearly what your results show. Refer to the evidence you have collected and your original aim.

Evaluation

This is a critical look at how effective your plan and action has been.

- What was your original aim?
- Did you achieve it?
- Was it a suitable aim?
- Was the method chosen suitable?
- Are the results relevant to the aim?
- Are the results clearly presented?
- If you started again, what would you do differently and why?
- What new areas have been uncovered for further study?
- Is there something you are particularly pleased with about your investigation?

The need for food

The body needs food for the following functions:

Growth and repair

Energy production

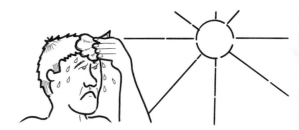

The control and regulation of body processes

If a substance does not maintain any of these functions it is not a food.

What is a food?

Food comes from animals and plants. Many foods are solid and some are liquid. All food contains at least one **nutrient** and some foods such as milk, bread, fish and soya beans contain a variety of nutrients. A nutrient is a chemical substance in a food that provides a particular function in the body. These chemical substances are **proteins, fats, vitamins, mineral elements** and **carbohydrates**. The study of the effect that nutrients have on the body is called **nutrition**.

As well as solid food the body needs **water**. Blood is made up of 80% water. Blood transports the nutrients around the body. Water is also important because it helps to dissolve and digest many foods. Without water the body cannot stay alive for more than a few days, because it loses fluid in sweat, urine, tears and breath. The loss of moisture from exhaled breath is known as **respiration**. Therefore, each day this loss must be replenished by drinking plenty of fluids.

Food contains water, but not enough for the daily bodily requirements. For good health it is essential to eat a variety of foods to obtain all the nutrients that the body needs. This is known as eating a **balanced diet**.

Recommendations for a balanced diet

In the United Kingdom there have been recommendations about dietary guidelines from groups that have received Government funding. Groups such as **NACNE** and **COMA** have been formed and **RDA's** and **Dietary Goals** have been put forward.

NACNE

The National Advisory Committee on Nutrition Education recommends that the population should:

1   Reduce fat, salt and sugar;
2   Reduce alcohol intake;
3   Increase intake of dietary fibre.

RDA's or RDI's

The Recommended Daily Allowance or Intake was published in 1979 by the Department of Health and Social Security. These give figures of the average amounts of food, energy and nutritive requirements for different groups of the population.

Dietary Goals

These are concerned with a healthy balance of nutrients in the diet. The recommendations are not in specific amounts as in RDA's.

The goals state that:

1   Babies should be breast-fed if it is possible.
2   As obesity is a health hazard, people should try to eat balanced diets to avoid problems with being overweight.
3   Everyone should increase their intake of dietary fibre and decrease their intake of fat, sugar, salt and alcohol.

COMA

The Committee of the Medical Aspects of Food Policy published a report for the DH in 1984. The recommended diets were related to cardio-vascular disease and stated that:

1   Fat and salt should be decreased;
2   The intake of fibre should be higher;
3   Large quantities of alcohol should be avoided;
4   Sugar intake of the population should not be increased.

Not everyone has a balanced diet. This may be a result of a lack of food resources being available or making the wrong food choices.

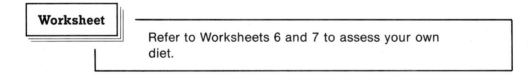

Worksheet

Refer to Worksheets 6 and 7 to assess your own diet.

Lack of food resources

In some developing countries, where there is a lack of food, only a few staple foods are available such as rice in India. The people may suffer from **malnutrition**, this is a result of eating only a small number of foods that do not contain all the essential nutrients.

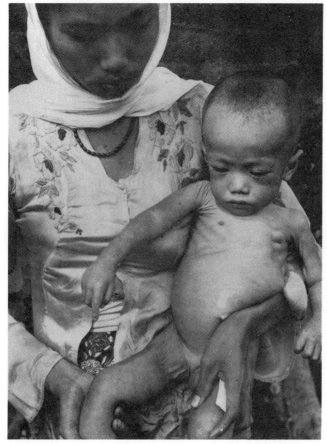

This child is suffering from **kwashiorkor** which is caused by a lack of protein in the diet. The child has a pot belly, swollen with water.

If people do not get enough food, their bodies do not receive sufficient amounts of any nutrients and this is known as **subnutrition**. Eventually lack of food leads to **starvation** and death.

Making the wrong food choices

There are many reasons for this, of which some will include:
- Lack of knowledge and understanding of dietary requirements;
- Poor and unadventurous meal planning;
- Likes and dislikes.

Energy and food

Our bodies use food to provide energy in order to live and be active. The body needs energy all the time, even when we are asleep, to maintain breathing and heart beat. Energy is not a nutrient. Proteins, fats and carbohydrates (starches and sugars) release energy for the body to use, these are broken down during the process of digestion. Food is turned into energy by a process called **oxidation**.

Oxidation

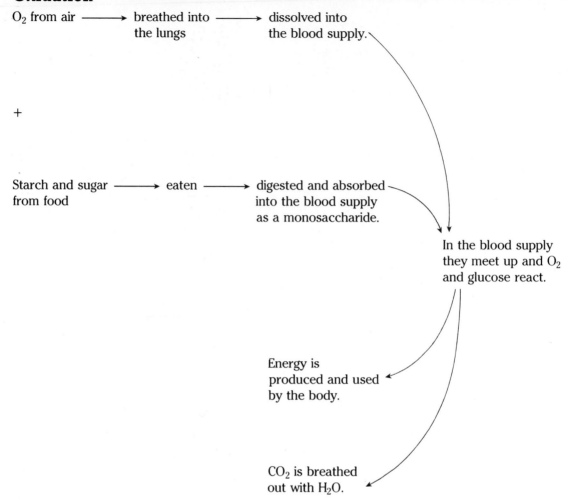

O_2 from air ⟶ breathed into ⟶ dissolved into
the lungs the blood supply.

+

Starch and sugar ⟶ eaten ⟶ digested and absorbed
from food into the blood supply
as a monosaccharide.

In the blood supply
they meet up and O_2
and glucose react.

Energy is
produced and used
by the body.

CO_2 is breathed
out with H_2O.

The correct chemical formula for this is:

$$6O_2 \quad + \quad C_6H_{12}O_6 \longrightarrow \text{energy} + 6CO_2 \quad + \quad 6H_2O$$

Oxygen + glucose ⟶ energy + carbon + water
dioxide

This reaction never stops because the body needs energy all the time for movement and heat. The rate at which our bodies use up energy is called the **metabolic rate**.

How is this energy measured?

Energy is measured in **kcal** or **kJ**, that is kilocalories or kilojoules.

1 kJ = 1000 joules
1 kcal = 1000 calories

4.2 kJ = 1 kcal.

To stay alive you need four kilojoules a minute.

Proteins

As can be seen from the illustration above **proteins** come from both **animal** and **plant** sources.

Protein is needed by the body for:

Growth and repair

It can also be used to provide:

Energy production

Every cell in the body contains protein.

Proteins are made up of **amino acids**. These contain hydrogen, oxygen, nitrogen and sometimes sulphur and phosphorus.

There are many kinds of amino acid and the body can convert them into the ones it needs. However there are **eight essential amino acids** that cannot be made by the body. Proteins from vegetable sources do not contain all the essential amino acids but if foods are combined together, e.g. baked beans on toast, these deficiences can be overcome. Therefore, one food can make up for what is missing in another food.

What happens if the body does not receive enough protein?

If there is a lack of protein in the diet then **PEM** or **protein energy malnutrition** occurs. This is because all the protein is used for energy and there is insufficient for its other functions.

This does not often happen in the UK, but in less-developed countries **kwashiorkor** and **marasmus** can occur.

Recommended Daily Intake of protein

CHILDREN		ADULTS		
0–2 years	30 g	**Women**		
2–5 years	40 g	18–35	Most occupations	55 g
5–9 years	50 g		Active occupations	65 g
		Over 55		50 g
Boys		**Men**		
9–12 years	70 g	18–35	Sedentary occupations	70 g
12–15 years	70 g		Active occupations	80 g
		35–36	Sedentary occupations	65 g
Girls			Active occupations	80 g
9–18 years	55 g	Over 65		60 g

Protein alternatives
See the section on meat substitutes, Chapter 7 on page 80.

Fats

Fat is needed by the body for:

Energy production

Warmth (fat acts as an insulator — because it is stored under the skin)

Satisfying the appetite
(this is because it is digested
slowly and stops hunger pangs)

Carrying fat soluble vitamins A, D, E and K

Fats are made up of **fatty acids** and **glycerol** that contain carbon, hydrogen and oxygen.

Fats can be divided into three groups:

saturated fatty acids,
unsaturated fatty acids or **mono unsaturated fatty acids**
and **polyunsaturated fatty acids**.

Saturated fatty acids

A saturated fatty acid chain:

```
       H   H   H   H   H   H
       |   |   |   |   |   |
   — C — C — C — C — C — C —
       |   |   |   |   |   |
       H   H   H   H   H   H
```

As these fatty acids are saturated they will not absorb any more hydrogen. A diet high in saturated fats is believed to increase the risk of heart disease, on account of its **cholesterol** content. This is a substance that is deposited in the arteries causing them to become narrower. This makes the blood flow more slowly and so increases the risk of a blood clot forming that can cause a heart attack.

Types of saturated fats

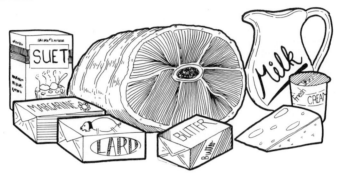

Unsaturated fatty acids

An unsaturated fatty acid chain:

```
       H   H   H   H   H   H
       |   |   |   |   |   |
   — C — C — C = C — C — C —
       |   |           |   |
       H   H           H   H
```

As unsaturated fatty acids contain one double bond they are able to react with some more hydrogen to become saturated.

Types of unsaturated fats

Polyunsaturated fatty acids

A polyunsaturated fatty acid chain:

$$\begin{array}{cccccc}
H & H & H & H & H & H \\
| & | & | & | & | & | \\
-C = C - C = C - C = C -
\end{array}$$

A polyunsaturated fatty acid has many double bonds and so is able to react with even more hydrogen to become saturated.

Types of polyunsaturated fats

What happens if the body has too much fat?

Too much fat in the diet can cause people to become overweight which may lead to **obesity**. This causes strain on the heart and can lead to a heart attack.

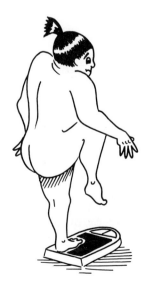

Carbohydrates

Carbohydrates are needed by the body for:

Energy production

Digestion

Carbohydrates contain carbon, hydrogen and oxygen.

There are three types of carbohydrates:

MONOSACCHARIDES
or simple sugars

Glucose found in fruits, honey, onions and sweetcorn.
Fructose found in fruit.
Glactose found in milk.

DISACCHARIDES

Sucrose found in cane and beet sugar.
Lactose from milk sugar.
Maltose found in cereals.

POLYSACCHARIDES

Cellulose or dietary fibre found in whole cereals, fruit and vegetables.

Too much carbohydrate in the diet results in people becoming overweight and possibly obese.

Investigation

Level 1

Sugar is often termed an empty food. This is because it only provides energy. Too much sugar causes tooth decay and obesity. In some foods there are 'hidden' sugars. This means that you do not expect them to be there.

Investigate the foods that contain these hidden sugars by visiting your local supermarket and looking at the food in your home. Make a chart to show the results and evaluate them.

Worksheet

Carry out the experiments on Worksheets 1–4 to determine the nutrient content of certain foods and then complete the table on Worksheet 5.

Dietary fibre

This is found in the cell walls and skins of fruits, cereals and vegetables. It should be eaten as part of a balanced diet. Dietary fibre does not change as it passes through the body during digestion. It helps to keep the waste matter soft so that it does not get lodged in the intestine and cause **constipation**.

What happens if the body does not have enough dietary fibre?

Constipation can be a direct result of lack of dietary fibre. Linked with this can be **heart disease** and **diverticulosis**. In diverticular disease the inner lining of the colon (part of the large intestine) becomes inflamed. Dietary fibre can remedy this.

Vitamins

At the turn of this century between 1900 and 1920, doctors discovered that there were extremely small amounts of substances present in some foods that were essential to good health. These were later called **vitamins**.

Vitamins are classified as:

water-soluble vitamins, such as the B group and vitamin C;

fat-soluble vitamins, such as vitamins A, D, E and K.

Vitamins help to prevent disease and ensure that other nutrients function properly. Usually a **well-balanced diet** will contain all the necessary vitamins. However, some foods are poor sources of certain vitamins, so it is important to choose foods carefully.

Fortified foods

Some processed foods are **fortified** or **enriched** to make their nutritional value the same as natural foods.

Vitamin supplements

The food we eat should be chosen carefully to ensure a balanced diet and should not need to be supplemented with vitamin pills.

Pregnant women take vitamin supplements for their growing baby with the consultation of their doctor. Tablets may be supplied which contain vitamins. Mothers are advised, however, to rely on a good diet before conception and during preganancy. Extra intake of vitamins can be gained by eating foods that contain them, e.g. if more vitamin A is needed then carrots or dark green vegetables could be eaten daily.

Minerals

Minerals are needed by the body to maintain health. There are 19 different minerals that are required by the body. Many are needed in very small amounts and are called **trace elements**.

Mineral supplements

If a balanced diet is eaten, mineral supplements should not be necessary.

Someone suffering from an illness such as anaemia may need iron tablets to supplement their diet. Pregnant women may be prescribed iron or calcium supplements by their doctor.

Vitamins

NAME	FUNCTIONS OF VITAMINS IN THE BODY	SOURCES	RESULTS OF DEFICIENCY	SPECIAL COMMENTS
VITAMIN A	Required to enable visual purple in the retina of the eye to be manufactured. This enables people to see in dim light. Helps to regulate growth. Keeps skin healthy and the linings of the body moist.	Margarine, milk, cheese, oily fish, liver, green vegetables, carrots, tomatoes, cod liver oil, halibut liver oil	Skin disorders and night blindness (*exeropthalmia*).	Fat-soluble vitamin. Stable in cooking and storing. This vitamin has surplus stored in the body in the liver.
VITAMIN B Thiamin B_1 Riboflavin B_2 Nicotinic Acid B_3 Pyridoxine B_6	Releases energy from sugars and starches (B_1), from amino acids (B_2). Keeps skin, tongue, digestive system healthy. Necessary for formation of haemoglobin (red blood cells).	Meat, cereals, dairy produce, eggs, yeast extracts, raw green salad vegetables, liver, kidney	Severe deficiency of thiamin B_1 results in beriberi. Severe deficiency of nicotinic acid B_3 leads to pellagra pyridoxine (B_6) deficiency which leads to anaemia, depression.	Water-soluble vitamin riboflavin, destroyed by sunlight. When meat is thawed from frozen, vitamin B_1 is lost in fluid. Thiamin B_1 is destroyed by heat.
VITAMIN C Ascorbic acid	Makes the connect tissue in flesh. Heals wounds, builds new tissue. Absorption of iron.	Blackcurrants, citrus fruits, green leafy vegetables, potatoes, especially new potatoes	Wounds do not heal, bruises develop easily, gums bleed, scurvy.	Water-soluble vitamin oxidises easily in air or during cooking process. Peel vegetables and fruit very thinly, otherwise Vitamin C is lost in the peelings. This vitamin is the most sensitive to loss.
VITAMIN D Calciferol	Needed for the absorption of calcium and phosphorus for healthy formation of bones and teeth.	Margarine, oily fish, liver, dairy products, sunshine	Rickets, osteomalacia, bones and teeth become decalcified.	Fat-soluble vitamin. Ergosterol found beneath the skin is converted to vitamin D by the action of sunlight on the skin. Stable in cooking and sunlight.
VITAMIN E Tocopherol	Not fully understood.	Wholegrain cereals, eggs, vegetable oils	Little is known.	Fat-soluble. Stable in cooking.
VITAMIN K	Coagulation of the blood.	Green leafy vegetables, liver, nuts, fruits	Little is known.	Fat-soluble. Stable in cooking.

Minerals

NAME	FUNCTIONS OF MINERALS IN THE BODY	SOURCES	RESULTS OF DEFICIENCY	SPECIAL COMMENTS
CALCIUM	Forms strong bones and teeth. Helps the working of muscles and nerves. Helps blood to clot on wounds to activate certain enzymes.	Milk, cheese, egg yolks, canned fish, broccoli, parsley, spinach, watercress	Rickets.	Vitamin D needs to be present for the absorption of calcium. Cooking and storage do not effect calcium.
IRON	To keep the haemoglobin (red blood cells) healthy. Haemoglobin carries oxygen around the body.	Liver, red meat, wholemeal bread, egg yolk, dried fruit, dark green vegetables	Anaemia.	Babies are born with six months supply of iron in their liver. Vitamin C aids absorption of iron. Cooking and storage do not effect iron. Too much gives constipation.
PHOSPHORUS	To build strong bones and teeth. It works in conjunction with calcium.	Found in most protein foods and is added to some processed foods.	Not known.	Cooking and storage do not effect phosphorus.
IODINE	To form thyromine hormones in the thyroid gland in the neck.	Tap water, iodised salt, sea foods, vegetables	Goitre which is the enlarging of the thyroid gland.	Found in soil and passes to plant foods and then to animals.
POTASSIUM & SODIUM	Control the amounts of water in the body.	Potassium: meat, fish, fruit, vegetables Sodium: common salt, all sea-foods, vegetables	Too little salt causes muscular cramps. (It is possible that sodium is connected with high blood pressure, if taken in excess). It is unlikely that there would be a deficiency as all body cells contain potassium.	Neither is reduced by cooking or heat and storage.
FLUORINE	Strengthens enamel on teeth.	Fluoridated drinking water, seafoods, tea	Softening of enamel on teeth.	Too much fluoride can cause enamel to pit and discolour.

Recommended Daily Intakes for vitamins and minerals

	VITAMIN A	THIAMIN	RIBOFLAVIN	NICOTINIC ACID	VITAMIN C	VITAMIN D	CALCIUM	IRON
Children	1–7 300 mg	1–7 0.6 mg 11–18 0.8 mg	1–7 0.8 mg 11–18 1.5 mg	1–7 9 mg 11–18 16 mg	1–11 25 mg 11–18 30 mg	1–6 10mg	1–8 600 mg 11–14 600 mg	1–8 7 mg 11–15 12 mg
Adults	750 mg	0.9 mg	1.4 mg	30 mg	30 mg		750 mg	10 mg
Lactating women	1200 mg	1.1	1.8 mg	60 mg	60 mg	10 mg	1200 mg	1200 mg
Pregnant women	—	1.0	1.8 mg	60 mg	60 mg	10 mg	1200 mg	1200 mg

 Investigation

Level 2

Referring to the NACNE recommendations, see how far they are met in your family. To do this carry out a survey of a week's shopping. Use a table to record your findings. Evaluate the results.

Level 3

Choose one of the following people and investigate ways in which a normal diet would have to be changed to suit their particular needs:

- A diabetic
- A person with heart disease
- A person with coeliac disease (this means that they have an intolerance to wheat protein or **gluten**).

Reading list and further sources of information:

NACNE Report *(1983)*
Health Education Council
78 New Oxford Street, London WC1A 1AH

Diet 2000 *(Pan, 1984)*
Dr Alan Maryon-Davis and June Thomas

The Manual of Nutrition *(1988)*
HMSO

COMA Report *(No. 28, 1984)*
DH *report on health and social subjects*

How to Fight Heart Disease
Quaker Oats Information Bureau
PO Box 24, Bridge Rd, Southall, Middlesex UB2 4AG

Dietary Fibre: a Guide to Sensible Eating
Kellogg Co, GB Ltd
Stretford, Manchester M32 8RA

The High Fibre Cook Book *(Dunitz, 1982)*
Pamela Westland

Video
You Are What You Eat
Flour Advisory Bureau
21 Arlington St. London SW1A 1RN

Fibre One Step To Healthier Living
Kellogg's, PO Box 100, Altringham, Cheshire WA14 5SZ

Computer Software
Microdiet *(nutritional analysis of foods)*
Longman Group Ltd
Burnt Mill, Harlow, Essex

Energy Food and Fitness *(balancing diets)*
Allinson Wholemeal Bread Education Service
Vanwall Rd, Maidenhead, Berkshire SL6 4UF

2 Energy

All energy starts from the sun. It is impossible to make energy or destroy it, but it is possible to change one kind of energy into another. Look at the example below.

Solar energy (energy from the sun's rays) provides:

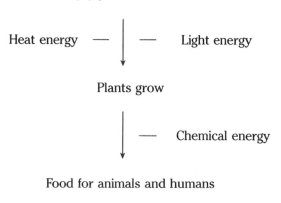

Heat energy — | — Light energy

Plants grow

| — Chemical energy

Food for animals and humans

Heat energy — | — Movement energy

The body functions

It is also possible to store energy and use it later, e.g. an athlete or swimmer stores energy to use it in a race.

Energy in the home

Energy is used in the home to provide heating and lighting, to cook food and to run electric and gas appliances. Up to 95% of the energy produced to heat the home could be lost if the home was not insulated.

These houses may look well cared for; it is not easy to see where energy is lost by wasting heat.

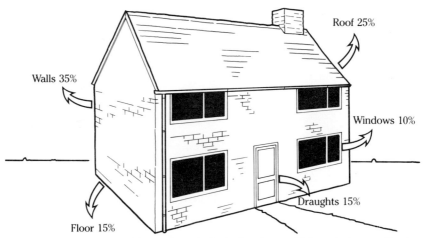

Roof 25%

Walls 35%

Windows 10%

Draughts 15%

Floor 15%

Always give priority to the places which are losing most heat.

 # Investigation

Level 2
Investigate ways of preventing heat loss in the home. Display the information in an attractive and informative way for the consumer. Think of a means of evaluating the information you have produced.

Heat, energy and cooking

In cooking, heat energy is passed to the food by three methods: **conduction**, **convection** and **radiation**. Most foods are cooked by a mixture of these methods.

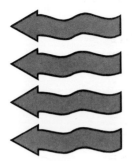

This illustration shows the movement of heat energy through a material. The heat passes from an area of higher temperature to an area of lower temperature, e.g. heat passes from the outside of a piece of food to the centre by conduction. Good conductors let heat pass through easily, poor conductors do not.

This illustration shows the transfer of heat by the circular movement of gas particles or liquids. The heated particles rise and the cooler particles fall to take their place, setting up convection currents with a gas or liquid, e.g. air in an oven is heated by convection currents.

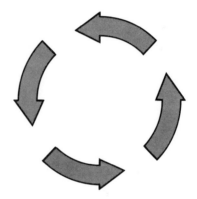

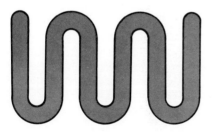

Radiation is the transfer of heat from its source in an electro-magnetic wave until it falls on an object in its path, e.g. microwaves penetrate food creating heat, but they will not directly heat the oven space or the container the food is in.

Worksheet

To demonstrate how conduction, convection and radiation take place, carry out the experiments on Worksheet 8, and then complete the chart of methods of cooking on Worksheet 9.

Cookers

Cookers are designed to carry out six basic cooking processes.

Baking
Roasting

Boiling
Stewing

Grilling

Frying

These basic cooking processes can be carried out on many different types of cookers.

Halogen hob

Slide-in gas oven

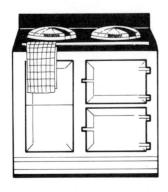

Aga or Rayburn

Low level electric grill and oven

'Baby Belling' cooker

Ceramic hob

Economical cooking

Economical cooking makes sense as it saves energy and money. Cookers are designed in such a way that both energy and money can be saved during cooking.

One example of this is **zone heating**. This works on the principle that hot air rises. So if the oven control is set at Regulo 4 or 180 °C, the centre of the oven will be at that temperature. The top of the oven will be hotter and the bottom of the oven cooler. This does not apply to fan ovens because the hot air is circulated constantly by the fan.

Thermostats

Thermostats are simple devices that control temperature.

A thermostat is able to react to the temperature of the air surrounding it. It then regulates the heat required in the appliance it is in. There are three types of thermostat in general use.

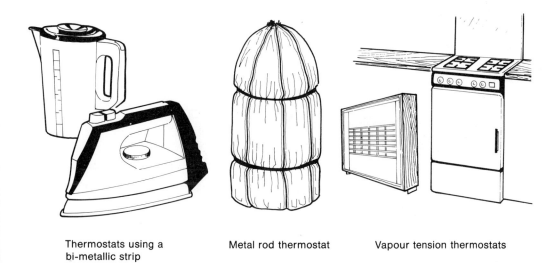

Thermostats using a
bi-metallic strip

Metal rod thermostat

Vapour tension thermostats

The principle of the thermostat is that gases, liquids and solids expand when heated and contract as they cool, that is, as the temperature drops.

Electricity & gas in the home

The meters you may have in your home are a domestic gas meter and an electricity meter. These can be outside in a box on the wall, or inside the house, often under the stairs.

The meter records the amount of gas or electricity used as it passes from the mains into your home.

Worksheet

Refer to Worksheets 10 and 11.
These will help you to read a meter and work out the cost of running gas and electric appliances.

What to do if there is a gas leak

1 Put out naked lights.
2 Do not turn any electric switches or plugs on or off.
3 Open doors and windows.
4 Check all gas taps are turned off.
5 Turn off gas supply at the meter.
6 Emergency Service — this can be found under GAS in the telephone directory.

 # Investigation

Level 3
What safety points should be remembered in the use and care of gas and electric ovens?

Microwave ovens

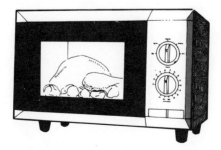

How a microwave oven works

A microwave oven is a box lined with metal which changes electric currents into microwaves when it is switched on. It operates through the electricity mains. The electric currents are changed by a device in the microwave oven called a magnetron.

What are microwaves?

These are similar to TV radio waves, in that they are also high frequency and short length.

Microwave cooking

In conventional cooking the outer surface of the food is heated and then the heat is **conducted** towards the inside or the middle of the food or liquid.

Microwaves cause heat by **friction**. This also happens when hands are rubbed together.

The microwaves cause the molecules in food to vibrate and this friction causes the temperature to rise. Some waves will go directly to the food, whilst others will be reflected off the metal walls and flooring, to be directed towards all the different surfaces of the food.

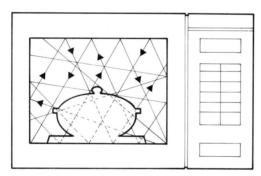

Microwave ovens and safety

If microwaves are not contained inside the cooking compartment, they can be dangerous to the user. Leakage of microwaves can come through the oven door. An appliance can be bought to test for leakage. Never lift the oven by the door. All manufacturers are very careful to build in safety factors. A microwave oven should be checked at least once a year.

Pressure cookers

How a pressure cooker works

The principle of pressure cooking is that when the cooker is heated, the water inside evaporates and the air inside expands. This causes the pressure to rise. Unlike a conventional saucepan, the lid of a pressure cooker is strongly sealed with a centre vent and safety valve. The increasing pressure building up inside the cooker raises the boiling point of the water to make steam. The food therefore cooks more quickly.

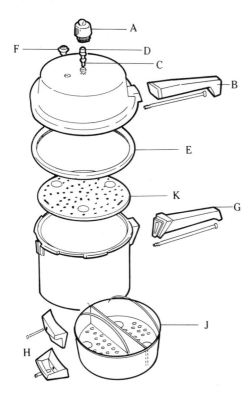

A   Set of weights

B   Cover handle and bolt

C   Centre vent and nut

D   Weight support

E   Gasket

F   Safety plug

G   Body handle and bolt

H   Front grip handle and screw

J   Perforated separator

K   Trivet

The centre vent can have different weights to give high, medium or low pressures; on some models this can be achieved by a dial.

The pressure cooker and safety

 As can be seen from the diagram of the pressure cooker, there is a safety valve in the lid. This safety valve ensures that the cooker cannot over-pressurise. If this happens, the valve comes out of the lid and the pressure is therefore reduced.

Alternative sources of energy

In this chapter we have looked at the use of energy in the home, particularly in cooking and running appliances. It is also important in heating the home, yet as fossil-based fuel resources such as oil, natural gas and coal are rapidly being used up, investigations are underway to find alternative sources of energy. Two alternative sources already in use are nuclear power and hydroelectric power. Nuclear energy is an attractive prospect economically as one tonne of uranium provides at least as much energy as two million tonnes of coal, but there are other more controversial issues to consider.

Investigation

Level 3

Investigate nuclear and hydroelectric power and write briefly under these headings:

1 Health and safety

2 Effects on the environment

Hydroelectric power relies upon a mountainous site with heavy and reliable rainfall as the flow of water is needed to turn the turbines to generate the electricity. This form of power would not be a suitable energy source for all domestic use in Great Britain, because of the lack of mountains and rainfall!

Energy sources for the future include harnessing wind power, solar power, wave power, tidal power and geo-thermal power.

Investigation

Level 3

Choose one of the energy sources above and investigate its acceptability as a future source of energy for domestic use.

Level 2

In a fan-assisted electric oven the temperature should remain constant irrespective of the position within the oven space. However in a conventional oven the top of the oven space will always be hotter than the area below. Investigate the reason for this and devise a simple experiment based on a baking task to test this theory. Record your results clearly and evaluate your work.

Reading list and further sources of information:

The British Gas Education Service
PO Box 46, Hounslow, Middlesex TW4 6NF

The Electricity Council
30 Millbank, London SW19 4RD

Complete Microwave Cookbook
Family Microwave Cookery
Pressure Cookery *(Ebury Press, 1986)*
Good Housekeeping

The WI Book of Microwave Cookery *(Ebury Press, 1985)*
Mary Norvak

Video
Microwave and Combination Ovens
Oxo Microwave Advisory Service
Tel: 0345–581810

Computer Software
CEDRIC
British Gas PLC
326 High Holborn, London WC1V 7PT

The Energy Factor
The Electricity Council
(address above)

Domestic Heating *(Longmans Press)*
5 Bentink Street, London W1

3 Food commodities

The main foods eaten in this country can be grouped into four kinds: meat and fish, cheese, eggs and milk, cereals and fruit and vegetables.

Cereals

Cereal in the form of bread is a staple food of the UK diet, yet other cereal products are increasing in popularity. Examples are given in this chapter.

Rice

The three main types of rice grown are short-grain or pudding rice, medium-grain and long-grain rice. In recent years, long-grain rice used in savoury dishes has become more popular.

Type of rice	Process
White rice, medium to long-grain	The husk and bran have been removed. On cooking the grains tend to separate.
Brown or whole-grain rice	The husk has been removed but the bran remains.
Easy-cook rice	The rice has undergone a steam pressure process which hardens the grain and prevents over-cooking. Both white and brown easy-cook rice is available.
Short-grain rice	The grains have a short, fat shape. It is softer than long-grain rice and when cooked, the grains tend to stick together.

Composition of rice

(Average values in 100 g cooked rice)

	BROWN RICE	WHITE RICE	PARBOILED RICE
Water (per cent)	70.3	72.6	73.3
Calorie Value	119	109	106
Protein (g)	2.5	2.0	2.1
Fat (g)	0.6	0.1	0.1
Carbohydrate: Total (g)	25.5	24.2	23.3
Fibre (g)	0.3	0.1	0.1
Ash (g)	1.1	1.1	1.1
Calcium (mg)	12	10	19
Phosphorus (mg)	73	28	57
Iron (mg)	0.5	0.2	0.4
Potassium (mg)	70	28	43
Thiamine (vit. B1) (mg)	0.09	0.02	0.03
Riboflavin (vit. B2) (mg)	0.02	0.01	0.01
Niacin (vit. PP) (mg)	1.4	0.4	0.8

 # Investigation

Level 1

1 Which type of rice provides the most protein, iron and B vitamins?
2 Which type of rice provides the most calcium?

Pasta

Pasta is the Italian term used to describe the various shapes made from the basic ingredients of wheat and water. The shapes include spaghetti, macaroni, tagliatelle, shells, bows, twists and lasagne.

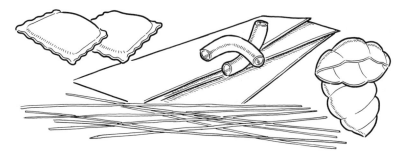

Sometimes small quantities of egg, tomato or spinach are added to the wheat paste, providing a variety of coloured pasta. Green or *verdi* pasta contains spinach and red pasta contains tomato. Brown or wholewheat pasta is also available. As with brown rice, the bran has not been removed in the processing.

The wheat used in pasta-making is a hard wheat known as durum; this is used so that the pasta remains separate and will not become floury and sticky once it is cooked. The wheat is ground to semolina, water is added and the dough is kneaded to develop the gluten, as with kneading in the bread-making process. The dough is forced through a metal plate with shaped holes, according to the type of pasta. The pasta dough is then cut to size by mechanical blades. The shapes are finally dried and packaged.

Nutritional composition of pasta (per 100 g)

Energy	1424 kJ
Protein	11 g
Carbohydrate	75 g
Fat	1 g

Both rice and pasta are versatile foods. They can be stored for long periods, provided they are kept dry in an airtight container. Pasta may be used in soups, salads and main dishes. Rice is a useful ingredient in salads, main dishes and puddings. They are relatively quick and easy to prepare, provided the instructions on the packet are followed.

Flour

Flour is another versatile food, it may be used to make pastry, bread, biscuits, cakes and puddings, as well as to thicken sauces. There are three basic types of flours.

Flour	Extraction
Wholemeal or wholewheat	100 % of the wholewheat grain
Brown	Approximately 85 % of the wheat grain
White	Approximately 75 % of the wheat grain, the bran and wheatgerm have been removed.

However the choice of flours is varied.

Plain	This flour is used when a chemical raising agent is not needed, e.g. in shortcrust and choux pastries, batters and for thickening sauces.
Self-raising	A chemical raising agent has been added, it is suitable for cakes and puddings.
Sponge (soft)	A light flour with a low-protein content which produces a small volume mixture, suitable for cakes, biscuits and shortcrust pastry. It gives a light or short texture.
Strong	Made from strong wheat, it has a high protein (gluten) content which produces a large volume and open texture. It is suitable for bread-making and flaky and puff pastries.
Stoneground	This is made by the traditional method of grinding the wheat grains between two stones.
Malted (granary)	Added grains of malted wheat give a distinctive texture and nutty flavour to this flour.

These flours are available in the following extraction rates:

Wholewheat	100 % extraction
Brown	85 % extraction
White	75 % extraction

A new 81 % extraction variety aimed at bridging the gap between brown and white flours is also available.

Nutritional composition of flour

NUTRIENT	WHITE	BROWN	WHOLEWHEAT
Protein (g)	11.3	11.8	12.0
Carbohydrate (g)	71.5	68.5	64.3
Fibre (g)	3.15	7.87	11.2
Fat (g)	1.0	1.6	2.4
Iron (mg)	2.2	3.6	3.5
Calcium (mg)	140	150	30
Thiamin (mg)	0.3	0.4	0.4
Nictonic acid (mg)	2.0	4.2	5.5

As vitamins and minerals are removed in the lower extraction flours, iron, thiamin and nicotinic acid must be added by law to all flours, to the level naturally present in 80% extraction flour. Calcium is added to all flour types except wholemeal and self-raising flours.

 # Investigation

Level 2

Bread is a staple food in the UK diet. Many different cultures have their own special types of bread. Find out which cultures the following types of bread are associated with and how they are served.

1 Bagels
2 Naan bread
3 Croissants
4 Pumpernickel bread
5 Pitta bread
6 Soda bread
7 Brioche
8 Rye bread
9 Challah
10 Chapati

Worksheet

Carry out a class experiment to determine the most suitable flour(s) for bread-making; refer to Worksheets 12–14.

Breakfast cereals

Breakfast cereals are a convenient food made from maize, rice, oats or wheat. They are generally eaten with milk and can provide a nutritious start to the day. They are very quick to prepare and it is possible for young children to serve themselves.

 Investigation

Level 1

As people have become more informed about the nutritional value of various foods, healthy eating is an important factor in their choice of diet.

Investigate this statement in relation to the choice of breakfast cereals on the market. Conduct your own survey. Your results could be shown as a histogram, pie graph or pictogram.

Refer to Worksheet 15 to record your results.

Fruit and vegetables

Fresh fruit and vegetables are an important part of our diet, because they provide fibre, vitamins and minerals. They are invaluable when planning meals as they add not only to the nutritive value of the meal, but also give colour to its appearance and add flavour, texture and aroma. Due to the high water content of most fruit and vegetables, they are a refreshing addition to any meal.

Nutritional values of fruit and vegetables

Good sources of vitamin A are provided by carrots, tomatoes, peaches, spinach, Brussels sprouts, cabbage, green beans and peas.

Good sources of vitamin C are provided by blackcurrants, oranges, lemons, grapefruit and tomatoes.

Good sources of dietary fibre are provided by baked beans, peas, spinach and dried fruits.

Potatoes are another staple food in the UK. They are valuable as a source of vitamin C, not because they contain a lot, but because we eat so many! Eating potatoes cooked in their skins also provides us with more fibre.

The choice of fruit and vegetables available in shops, supermarkets and on market stalls has increased to include many varieties from hot climates. This is due to improved storage and transport facilities. Some of these fruits and vegetables may be unfamiliar. Can you recognise the ones described here?

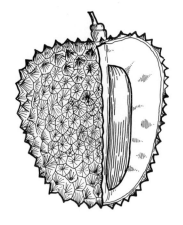

A fruit with a rough reddish-brown skin and pearly white juicy flesh. The flesh is lightly perfumed and there is a small stone in the centre. It is used in Chinese cooking and fruit salads. It can also be bought in cans.

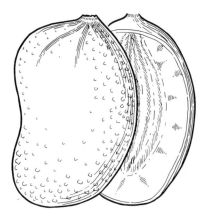

A fruit with a yellow flesh and a large flat stone in the middle. The skin may be yellowish-green or bright red. It is rich in vitamins A and C. It is used to make a chutney traditionally served with curries.

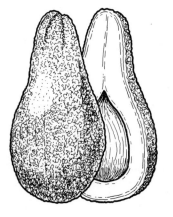

A pear shaped fruit with a dark green outer skin. The flesh is yellowish-green and it has a rich smooth texture and a bland taste. It has a high fat content and is generally served as a vegetable starter or in salads, soups and dips. It has a large stone in the centre.

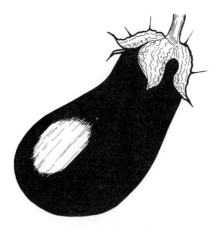

A vegetable with a smooth dark purple skin and creamy coloured flesh that darkens when cut. It is used as an ingredient of the traditional Greek dish, mousaka.

A variety of the marrow family. The average size is 10 to 20 cm long and 2 to 5 cm diameter. The colour is dark green but it often has a striped appearance with yellow flecks. It is served as a hot vegetable, and in soups, salads and casseroles.

 # Investigation

Level 1

Once you have identified the fruits and vegetables by name, find out their countries of origin (where they are grown) and how to store and prepare them. Use recipe books to find recipes that use the individual fruit or vegetable. Also try to discover where to buy them locally, at what time of the year they are available and how much they cost. You could choose some more unusual fruit or vegetables to investigate. You may like to try out some of the recipes you have researched.

Fruit and vegetables should be eaten as fresh as possible, as they are at their best nutritionally as well as looking and tasting good. If vegetables and fruit are eaten raw, as in salads, or are cooked for only a short time, they should retain most of their vitamin C content.

Stir-fry vegetables

This recipe involves cooking vegetables for just a short time.

You will need

100 g beansprouts

Carrot sticks

½ onion, diced

½ sliced pepper

1 stick celery

50 g mushrooms

15 g margarine

1 tablespoon soy sauce

Salt and pepper

(**NB** *It may be necessary to blanch the bean sprouts by plunging them into boiling water for one minute and then cooling them quickly in cold water. This ensures that harmful micro-organisms that may cause food poisoning are destroyed.*)

What do do

1   *Melt the margarine.*

2   *Fry the onion and carrot for 2–3 minutes, in a wok or large frying pan.*

3   *Add the celery and pepper and fry for 1 further minute.*

4   *Add the mushrooms and beansprouts, fry for 1 further minute.*

5   *Season, add soy sauce.*

6   *Serve on a hot dish.*

7   *Eat immediately.*

 # Investigation

Level 3

Investigate other quick ways of cooking vegetables by researching recipes or trying out your own experiments.

For example, you could compare different methods of cooking Brussels sprouts or green cabbage; both of which are rich in vitamin C. Your aim would be to find the most palatable result and discover which method retains the most vitamin C. Refer to Worksheet 16 to find out how to do the vitamin C test.

Home Economists suggest the following rules for using, storing and cooking vegetables, to retain the vitamin C content.
- Vegetables should be eaten as fresh as possible.
- Do not pre-soak vegetables before cooking.
- Do not chop vegetables too finely.

- Only peel vegetable skins if they are tough or blemished.
- Boil cooking water before placing vegetables into it.
- Cook vegetables in a small amount of water.
- Vegetables should be firm, not waterlogged, do not overcook them.
- Do not add bicarbonate of soda to the cooking water.
- Add very little or no salt to the cooking water.
- Use the cooking water to make gravy.
- Do not cook vegetables in advance and keep them warm until needed.

 Investigation

Level 2

Many children do not like vegetables because their experience of soggy, waterlogged cabbage and overcooked carrots has not encouraged them to try these and other vegetables again.

Plan, cook and serve a lunch for yourself and a child of primary school age (five to eleven years old) to show an imaginative use of vegetables. The meal should appeal to you both and show your understanding and awareness of good vegetable preparation and cooking.

Fruit and vegetables are seasonal foods. Many varieties such as strawberries, raspberries, peaches and Brussels sprouts are only available in their fresh state at certain times of the year. Root vegetables such as potatoes and fruits such as apples may be stored for several months in controlled low temperature conditions ensuring a supply throughout the year.

Fruit and vegetables are available as preserved foods. Sometimes the process is carried out commercially, e.g. canning, freezing and drying and when there is a seasonal glut, they may be processed by home preservation methods, e.g. freezing and jam-making.

In these forms fruit and vegetables become convenient food commodities, requiring very little preparation time or cooking expertise.

Pulses

Pulses are dried beans, peas and lentils, there are many varieties to choose from, including red kidney beans, chick peas, black eye beans, lentils, butter beans, cannellini beans, flageolet beans, haricot beans, soya beans, mung beans, and many more . . .

Dried pulses (except lentils) must be soaked before cooking, usually overnight in cold water or for two to three hours in boiled water. The cooking time varies between 30 minutes and three hours depending on the type used. However, cans of ready-to-use beans are a convenient and popular source.

Investigation

Level 1

Research recipe books and leaflets to find how pulses are used in cooking. Try looking at soups, salads and main course dishes.

Try to find out what special instructions must be followed when preparing and cooking red kidney beans and why these are necessary.

Nutritional value of pulses

Pulses have an important role in a healthy diet, particularly for vegetarians, as they are high in protein and dietary fibre and low in fat.

Research which varieties of pulse vegetables are available in the convenient canned form and compare the cost of canned pulses with dried pulses.

Dairy products and eggs

Milk — how do you choose?

The type of milk you choose depends on:
- The particular needs of the family or individual;
- Personal taste;
- Where you live in the world;
- What you want to use the milk for.

Choice 1 The source

In the UK we drink mostly cows' milk; however some people suffer from an allergy to milk from this source and so use goats' milk, whilst others just prefer the taste of goats' milk.

In Greece and some other Meditteranean countries, they also consume sheep's milk and this is made into yoghurt and cheese. Soya milk is also available and is used by strict vegetarians. Jewish families do not eat meat and drink milk with it, neither do they use milk and meat together in the same dish nor use a milk container or utensil for preparing a meat dish.

Choice 2 Whole milk, semi-skimmed milk or skimmed milk?

By analysing the information we can see that:

- All milk provides protein, vitamins and minerals.
- Skimmed and semi-skimmed milk contain as much protein, calcium and vitamin B_2 as whole milk, but have less fat.
- Semi-skimmed milk contains approximately half the fat of whole milk and skimmed milk has had almost all the fat removed.

	TOTAL FAT	SATURATED FAT	ENERGY CALORIES	PROTEIN	CALCIUM	VIT B_2	VIT A	VIT D
Whole milk	22.2 g	13.2 g	380	19.3 g	702 mg	1.11 mg	228 mg	0.13 mg
Semi-skimmed milk	10.5 g	6.3 g	280	19.5 g	729 mg	1.12 mg	104 mg	0.05 mg
Skimmed milk	0.6 g	0.3 g	195	19.9 g	761 mg	1.17 mg	Trace	Trace

We can make the following conclusions from the evidence.
- Skimmed milk is best for those people who want to cut down on their energy and fat intake and who do not want a creamy tasting milk.
- Semi-skimmed milk is chosen by people who want to cut down on their energy and fat intake but who still want a creamy tasting milk.
- Whole milk is chosen by those who prefer a creamy tasting milk. They may still be concerned about their energy and fat intake, but may choose to cut out other food products to achieve a healthy and balanced diet. Pregnant and nursing mothers choose this milk because they need vitamins A and D.

The Government recommends whole milk for the under fives. Skimmed milk is **not** suitable for children under the age of five years because of its lower content of energy and vitamin A. Semi-skimmed milk can, if you wish, be gradually introduced after the age of two years providing the child is receiving all the energy it needs from other food sources.

Choice 3 Processing and packaging

Untreated milk:
This milk must come from brucellosis accredited herds and whether sold in bottles or cartons must be labelled 'raw unpasteurised milk'. Most milk bought in the UK has been subjected to some form of heat treatment; this ensures the destruction of bacteria and improves the keeping qualities.

Pasteurised milk:
This milk will keep for one to two days in a cool place or three to four days in a refrigerator. At the dairy, the milk is subjected to a mild heat treatment of 72 °C for 15 seconds, rapidly cooled to not more than 10 °C and filled into bottles or disposable containers. This milk has a visible cream line and is ideal for drinking neat and using in drinks, in cooking and with cereals.

Homogenised milk:
This milk has no cream line. Before pasteurisation it is forced through a fine opening which breaks down the fat globules into small particles and so ensures they remain evenly distributed throughout the milk. It has a whiter appearance than ordinary pasteurised milk.

Channel Islands milk:
This milk is pasteurised and cooled as above, then filled into bottles. It is creamy milk with a definite cream line, produced by Jersey, Guernsey or South Devon breeds of cow. It has a high fat content.

Sterilised milk:
This milk, available whole or skimmed is sold in long-necked glass bottles or heat-resistant plastic bottles, it should keep unopened for a minimum of seven days without refrigeration, although several weeks is usual. Once opened it will keep as long as pasteurised milk.

The milk is first homogenised, then bottled, sealed and heated to above boiling point for 20–30 minutes, it is then cooled.

The colour and flavour is affected by the long heat treatment which causes **caramelisation** of the milk sugar or lactose. This milk is ideal for milk puddings and custard because of its creamy flavour.

Ultra heat treated milk:
This is 'Long Life' or UHT milk. It is homogenised and then heated to at least 132 °C for one second. It is then quickly cooled and packed into foil-lined cartons. It will keep unopened for six months and is ideal to keep as a standby at home or for self-catering holidays.

Sterilised and UHT milks are not recommended for lacto-vegetarians because the heat treatment process these types of milk undergo destroys considerable amounts of vitamin B_{12}. This is an important nutrient that lacto-vegetarians and vegans must ensure they get an adequate supply of, as its main food source is from animal flesh and animal products.

Investigation

Level 2
Investigate the varieties of packaging available for different types of milk. Compare the advantages and disadvantages of each type.

Cheese

Cheese comes in a variety of colours, textures, flavours and aromas and from many different countries. Each has its specialities.

Some are firm and well matured whilst others are soft and creamy. There are low-fat varieties such as Edam, cottage cheese, Quark and skimmed milk soft cheese. Some types are flavoured with herbs, garlic, mushrooms or peppers. *Fromage Frais* is a very soft cheese often flavoured with fresh fruit and eaten as a pudding. Cheese is an extremely versatile food and has many uses in cooking.

Investigation

Level 1

Research suitable types of cheese for each of the following uses.

1 Pizza topping
2 Sprinkling over spaghetti bolognese
3 Cheesecake
4 Cheese sauce

Cheese provides:

Protein
Calcium
Vitamin A ⎫
Vitamin D ⎬ the amounts vary according to the fat content of the cheese.
Fat ⎭
Energy

Making cheese
Cheese is made from milk. It is eaten raw or cooked, as a snack or at any meal. It is used in both sweet and savoury dishes.

To make a soft cheese

You will need

300 ml milk   *Saucepan*
½ large lemon   *Lemon squeezer*
Salt   *Colander*
                       Muslin or kitchen roll
                       Mixing bowl
                       Thermometer

What to do

1 *Pour the milk into a saucepan.*

2 *Heat the milk until it is warm (38 °C).*

3 *Squeeze the juice from the lemon.*

4 *Add the lemon juice to the milk and stir.*

5 *Allow to stand for 2 minutes.*
   *There should be a clear yellow liquid (**whey**) and white solid lumps (**curds**). If the whey is still milky add a little more lemon juice.*

6 *Line the colander with kitchen paper or damp muslin.*

7 *Place the colander over a mixing bowl and leave to drain for 30–40 minutes.*

8 *Add salt to the cheese and taste on crackers.*

Yoghurt

This is a popular food because it is so convenient and versatile. It is used as a snack food, as a food for people on the move, e.g. packed lunches, as a quick dessert and as a first solid food for babies. It is useful in cooking as a low-fat alternative to single cream. Yoghurt is a good source of protein and calcium.

Making yoghurt

You will need

560 ml milk
15 ml natural yoghurt
50 g dried milk powder (optional)
Choose one of these:
Sterilised milk
UHT milk
Boiled and cooled pasteurised milk
Boiled and cooled goats' milk

Saucepan
Thermometer
Tablespoon
Vacuum flask
Airtight container
Bowl

What do do

1 Pour the milk into a saucepan.

2 Heat the milk until it is warm (43 °C).

3 Blend the yoghurt into the warm milk, with the dried milk powder if this is to be used.

4 Rinse the vacuum flask out with boiling water to warm the flask.

5 Pour the milk and yoghurt into the flask, seal and leave for 7 hours.

6 Pour the yoghurt into a bowl and cool it quickly by standing the bowl in cold water and gently stirring the yoghurt.

7 Pour the yoghurt into an airtight container or leave it in the bowl, cover and refrigerate for approximately 4 hours before use. It will keep for 4–5 days if kept in the fridge.

You may use the yoghurt in salad dressing, on breakfast cereal and in cooking, or you could flavour it with puréed fruit.

 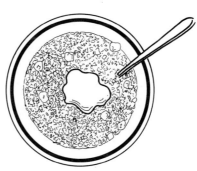

Investigation

Level 1
Investigate which type of milk makes the best yoghurt. Does the addition of dried milk powder improve it? Carry out a sensory appraisal using the chart below.

FOOD	SMELL	TASTE	TEXTURE
UHT			
Pasteurised			
Sterilised			
Goats' milk			
Dried milk powder added			

Level 2
Flavours can be added to natural yoghurt such as:

1 Fruit
2 Raisins
3 Coconut
4 Jam

How do these affect the nutritional content of the yoghurt? Evaluate your findings.

Eggs

Nutritional value
The white of an egg contains:

Protein
Riboflavin

The yolk of an egg contains:

Protein
Fat
Carotene (vitamin A)
Vitamin D
Riboflavin
Thiamin
Calcium
Phosphorus
Iron

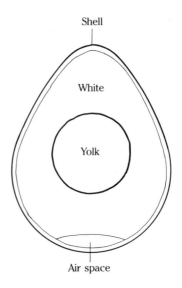

Shell

White

Yolk

Air space

Eggs have many uses in cooking.
- Binding: egg is added to mixtures to hold ingredients together, as in beefburgers, lentil croquettes and chicken rissoles.
- Thickening: eggs are combined with milk and then heated to thicken a mixture, such as egg custard, sauces and lemon curd.
- Adding air to a mixture: when egg whites are whisked, the protein partly coagulates and a foam is formed, with bubbles of air trapped inside a thin layer of set egg white. This foam is added to dishes to give them a light texture, e.g. whisked cake mixtures such as swiss roll, soufflé and mousse.
- Coating: some foods are coated with breadcrumbs, and egg is used to hold the crumbs onto the outside of the food. The egg also sets or coagulates quickly and prevents the cooking oil from soaking into the food. Scotch eggs, potato croquettes and fish cakes are examples of foods that are coated in this way.
- Enriching: eggs may be added to a mixture to add nutritive value to the dish, e.g. sometimes egg yolk is added to creamed potatoes or apple fool.
- Emulsifying: eggs are used in the production of mayonnaise because they form a film around the droplets of oil which are then held in suspension in water. This is the same principle as in the use of soap when washing hands.

Buying eggs

In the EEC eggs are graded according to size and quality, and this information is given on the packaging. The sizing is based on the weight of the egg in its shell, as shown below:

Weight	Size
Under 45 g	7
45–50 g	6
50–55 g	5
55–60 g	4
60–65 g	3
65–70 g	2
70 g and over	1

The majority of eggs on sale are Grade A. This means that they should be fresh and clean. The shell should be intact and the air pocket within the shell should be 6 mm or less.

Meat and fish

Meat

In Britain the three traditional meats eaten are beef, lamb and pork. Although for some, certain meats are forbidden by their religious laws, e.g. pork is not eaten by Jewish families and beef is not touched by Hindus as the cow is sacred in their religion. There are many different cuts of meat; some are suitable for quick cooking by processes such as grilling, barbecueing, stir-frying or microwaving, and are the most expensive. The less expensive cuts may be used in slow cooking casseroles.

Investigation

Level 2
Investigate which cuts of beef, pork and lamb are suitable for each cooking process.

Sometimes meat is processed to make it more convenient such as minced or cubed. Excess fat may also be trimmed from meat to give the consumer a leaner product, in line with NACNE recommendations to cut down on animal fat intake. Products such as low-fat sausages and lean minced beef are becoming increasingly popular.

There are numerous commercially made meat products such as pies, beefburgers, and salami. Some products are bought fresh, others frozen or canned.

Offal
The internal organs of animals, such as liver, kidney and heart are another food source and are particularly rich in iron.

Nutritional value of meat
Protein
Fat
Iron
Thiamin ⎫
Riboflavin ⎬ B vitamins
Niacin ⎪
B_{12} ⎭
Vitamin A

Birds that are eaten in Britain are grouped as poultry, which includes chicken, turkey, duck and goose, and game which includes pheasant, grouse, quail and partridge. Rabbit and hare are also classed as game.

 All frozen meats, in particular poultry, must be thoroughly defrosted before cooking to avoid the risk of food poisoning.

Fish

Fish is a very nutritious food, providing protein and minerals, however, it is undervalued by some. In Britain only about 1 kg of fresh fish per household is eaten in one year.

Fish may be cooked by poaching, frying, steaming, grilling, baking and barbecueing.

Fish is also available in cans, e.g. tuna, pilchards, salmon and sardines. If these canned fish are eaten with the softened bones they provide a good source of calcium and vitamin D. Frozen fish is also popular as the fish has been gutted, cleaned and filleted before packaging.

Nutritional value

Oily fish contains:

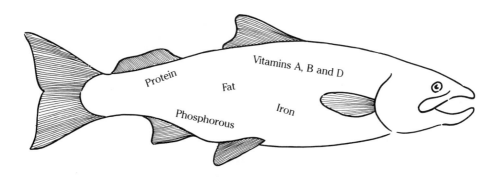

White fish contains:

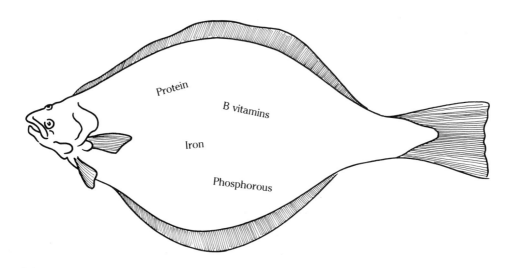

Shellfish contains:

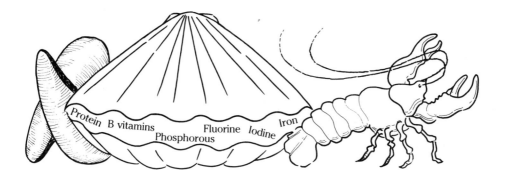

Investigation

Level 1
Investigate recipes for cooking fresh fish using some of the cooking processes given and try out the ones you think you may like.

Reading list and further sources of information:

British Meat Education Service
5 St John's Square, London EC1M 4DE

Sea Fish Information Service
144 Cromwell Road, London SW7 4ET

British Egg Information Service
Bury House, 126–128 Cromwell Road, London SW7 4ET

Dairy Produce Advisory Service
Thames Ditton, Surrey KT7 0EL

Flour Advisory Bureau
21 Arlington Street, London SW1A 1RN

US Rice Council
11–35 St John's Street, London EC1M 4AA

Tilda Rice
c/o Munro and Forster PR, 37 Soho Square, London W1

Fresh Fruit and Vegetable Information Bureau
126–128 Cromwell Road, London SW7 4ET

Potato Marketing Board
50 Hans Crescent, Knightsbridge, London SW1X 0NB

Video
British Food, Information of Food from Britain
542–544 Market Towers, New Covent Garden Market, London SW8 5NQ

The effects of cooking on food

In Chapter 2 you will have seen that heat energy is passed to food by three methods, **conduction**, **convection** and **radiation**. The foods that are heated by these methods change in structure as they are cooked.

Brainstorm in groups the reasons for cooking foods. Express your findings in the clearest way possible. You may wish to do this on card or a flip-chart, so that the work can be displayed.

Make the chart clear and easy to read.

Some key words to use are: palatability, texture, non-toxic, colour.

The effects of heat on certain foods

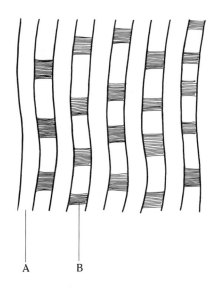

A   B

Meat

Meat is made up of muscle fibres (**A**) and connective tissue (**B**).

Muscle fibres contain protein, B vitamins and minerals. Connective tissue is responsible for the toughness of meat. It holds the muscle fibres together. When meat is cooked, the proteins coagulate, or set. They also change in construction, because they have been heated. This can be seen because the meat changes from red to brown. The proteins are then said to be **denatured**. This process is irreversible.

If meat used in a stew is cooked at too high a temperature, or boiled, then coagulation of the proteins is more rapid. They form a hard solid mass and the meat will be tough and difficult to digest. Therefore, meat cooked by this method needs slow, gentle heating to be successful.

Fish

Fish, like meat, is made up of muscle fibres and connective tissues. The muscle fibres are much shorter than in meat and there is less connective tissue. Fish, therefore, does not need a long cooking time.

Eggs

The coagulation of eggs occurs at a temperature below the boiling point of water. If eggs are heated for too long, the proteins are denatured and the eggs become rubbery.

Milk

When milk is heated, the proteins it contains coagulate to form a skin on the top of it. The air bubbles trapped in the milk can expand and lift the skin, causing the milk to boil over.

Cheese

When cheese is heated, it softens and the fat it contains separates out from the rest. If cheese is overcooked, the protein becomes tough and stringy like chewing gum. If cheese is grated and cooked on a moderate heat, then it is less likely to toughen.

Cheese mixes readily with many other dishes. The physical changes that occur when it is heated enables it to be used in a variety of ways, e.g. in sauces, soufflés, or mixed with other dishes to enrich them, such as potatoes.

Vegetables

When vegetables are cooked it is important that there is as little loss of vitamin C as possible. They should not, therefore, be overcooked. During the cooking process, the cellulose in the vegetables softens and the starch gelatinises.

 # Investigation

Level 2

On worksheet 16 you will see an explanation of how to do a vitamin C test. Choose a variety of methods of cooking vegetables and see which one produces the least vitamin C loss.

NB Choose vegetables that contain the most vitamin C. Use the food tables, (your teacher will supply these), to find out this information. Remember also that vitamin C can be lost by oxidation (old vegetables contain less vitamin C), peeling thickly (vitamin C is just below the skin), overcooking, or chopping too finely.

Test the water that the vegetables are cooked in. Record your results carefully and make an evaluation.

One of the reasons for cooking food is to make it non-toxic. Some foods contain substances that could cause an upset stomach if they are not treated properly. An example of this is red kidney beans. If these are not cooked thoroughly and properly then the toxic agents in the beans are not removed. Kidney beans are perfectly safe to eat if correct cooking procedures are used. Canned kidney beans have already been cooked and so do not require a lengthy cooking time. The manufacturer's instructions should be followed carefully.

Starches

Starches found in flours have the property of thickening liquids when they are heated. The starch granules absorb the heated liquid and swell. The mixture will then thicken and **gelatinisation** has taken place.

If this process of thickening liquids is not done properly, then the food will be lumpy or too thick or thin.

Starches that are in foods that are cooked by dry heat will go through three stages during the cooking processes, such as grilling, toasting or baking. The surface of the food will start to change colour to a light brown, that is known as **dextrinisation**. It will then go golden brown, known as **caramelisation** and if overcooked will go black, known as **carbonisation**.

Sugars

Sugars dissolve in water or liquid and can be used in this way to make syrup. When sugar is heated directly, it melts and caramelises. This property of sugar is used in the making of sweets and as a browning agent in many products.

Fats and oils

Fats and oils can be heated to a high temperature before any changes occur. At about 300 °C the fats will ignite. This is known as the

flashpoint.

If the flashpoint is reached and the fat or oil ignites, then the safety procedures are as follows.

1   Turn off the source of heat.
2   Cover the pan with a saucepan lid, chopping board or damp teatowel to cut off the source of oxygen in the air. This oxygen allows the burning process to continue freely.
3   **NEVER** place the hot fat under water or put water onto it. This will cause severe spitting and the water will evaporate into steam that will scald.

58

Investigation

Level 1
Experiment to investigate the changes that take place when potatoes are cooked by moist heat.

You will need
1 medium sized potato   *Medium saucepan and lid*
                                 Draining spoon
                                 Chopping knife

What do do

1   *Half fill the saucepan with water and heat until it boils.*

2   *Wash the potato and divide it into quarters, using the chopping knife.*

3   *Place the potato quarters into boiling water and note the time.*

4   *After 5 minutes remove one quarter.*
    (a) *Cut it in half and inspect.*   (b) *Draw what you see.*

5   *After 10 minutes remove another quarter.*
    Repeat (a) *and* (b) *in point* **4**.

6   *After 15 minutes remove a third quarter and repeat as above.*

7   *Leave the last quarter in the water until it is cooked. Record how long this took.*

Explain what has happened to the potato at each stage of the experiment.

What use could you make of your findings when cooking vegetables?

Boiling is a moist method of cooking, involving convection and conduction of heat. What other methods can be used to cook potatoes? Tabulate your results.

Refer to Worksheet 17 once you have finished this investigation.

Level 2
Experiment to compare the changes that take place when a cake mixture is baked in a conventional oven and cooked in a microwave oven.

You will need
1 packet of instant cake mix
Duralex® glasses, or heatproof glass ramekin dishes

What do do
Use ½ of the mixture for the microwave cooking. The other ½ should be baked.

Observe and record what happens during the cooking processes. (Use a conventional oven with a glass door and a light.)

Compare the cakes once cooked.

What use can you make of your findings when cooking cakes?

Refer to Worksheet 17 when you have finished this investigation.

Level 3

To find out what happens to food when it is heated under the grill, devise an experiment to look at the differences that occur when heat is transferred to these foods.

The selection you choose should come from each of the different food groups. You will need small quantities and remember to consider cost. Refer to the section on designing experiments on page 1.

Collate your findings carefully.

Make a table of your results.

Evaluate your work and report your findings back to the rest of the class.

Refer to Worksheet 18 once you have finished your investigation.

Convenience foods

What is a convenience food?

A convenience food is a commodity that is prepared so that time is saved by the people using it. This allows for more flexibility in their lifestyles.

Although convenience foods can provide easy to prepare nutritious foods, they can be expensive. They are best used with fresh foods and should not be a substitute for them. They may contain ingredients you do not wish to eat, so it is important to look at the ingredients on the food label remembering that

THE

ORDER

OF CONTENTS

IS IN

DESCENDING

ORDER

OF THE

QUANTITY USED.

 Investigation

Level 1
Ready-prepared chilled foods are becoming increasingly popular. Visit a local supermarket and make a list of all the ready-made meals in the chill cabinets. Note the weight and cost of these foods. Choose one of these meals and make a home-made version. Note the weight and cost. Compare your results and evaluate your findings. Use Worksheet 19 to record your results.

For and against convenience foods

+   −

A busy working person can save time in preparation by using convenience foods.

The length of time some convenience foods can be kept, or their 'shelf-life', is far longer than the same 'fresh' food.

Mixed with fresh foods, convenience foods can give extra variety and colour to meals.

If cooking facilities are poor then these foods can be useful.

If people have difficulty preparing foods, convenience foods can be an acceptable substitute.

Convenience foods can be useful when unexpected guests arrive.

Nutrients can be lost because of the cooking and preserving processes involved.

Unwanted additives can be added to prolong the shelf-life of the goods.

A preserved food can be more expensive than its equivalent fresh food.

Some frozen foods have a high percentage of water in them for which the consumer is paying.

The flavour and texture of some convenience foods are not as good as the same fresh food.

Some convenience foods need almost the same amount of preparation and cooking as their fresh equivalents.

Investigation

Working in pairs choose one of the following convenience foods to compare it with its home-made alternative.

Level 1
Custard powder
Cheese sauce
Milk shake

Level 2
Cake mix
Packet vegetable soup
Yorkshire pudding

Level 3
Shortcrust pastry
Bread roll mix
Lemon meringue pie

In the list below you will find the information you will need to make a suitable comparison.

Cost
Preparation Time
Preparation Skills
Equipment needed
Time of cooking
Finished result/taste/texture/appearance/smell
Advantages
Disadvantages

Evaluate the work that you have carried out.

Reading list and further sources of information:

Canned Food Information Centre
22 Greencoat Place, London SW1 1EG

Heinz Products
H.J. Heinz Co Ltd, 15–17 Huntsworth Mews, London NW1 6DD

National Spice and Herb Information Service
Cavendish House, 51–55 Mortimer Street, London W1N 7TD

Video
Food Glorious Food
International Tin Research Institute
Kingston Lane, Uxbridge, Middlesex, UB8 3PJ

6 Preservation

ASSESSMENT OBJECTIVES

2 3 4 5 6 7 8 9

Why are foods preserved?

Certain foods can be preserved so that when they are out of season, they can still be eaten. During the summer months there is often a plentiful supply or 'glut' of some foods, making them cheaper to use and economical to preserve. This enables our diet to be more varied.

What causes food to deteriorate?

In the air ———————— Micro-organisms ══════ Yeasts
                                                      Moulds
In food ———————— Enzymes   Bacteria

Micro-organisms

The micro-organisms that destroy food grow quickly at room temperatures. They can be destroyed by heat and acid and cannot survive in too dry conditions or too high a sugar or salt environment.

Enzymes

These are chemicals made inside the cells of all plants. They are **proteins**. Enzymes still continue to work even after the fruit or vegetables have been picked or an animal has been slaughtered. If they are left without treating in some way, enzymes cause the food to decay.

Some fruit and vegetables should be blanched before freezing to slow down enzyme activity.

Equipment used for preservation

Jam Chutney and Pickles

Make sure all old labels are removed. Wash and dry the jars thoroughly. Check for chips or cracks. Discard suspect jars.

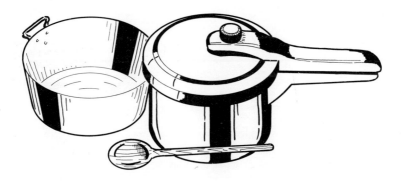

Preserving pan, long-handled wooden spoon and pressure cooker

A variety of lids can be used. Metal lids used for chutney or pickles should be plastic coated on the inside so that the acids in the preserves do not erode the metal lids. Clip-on plastic lids could also be used. Jam pot covers can be bought for jams. These are cellophane with waxed discs that are put straight onto the hot jam. The wax side is put down onto the jam to help form a seal.

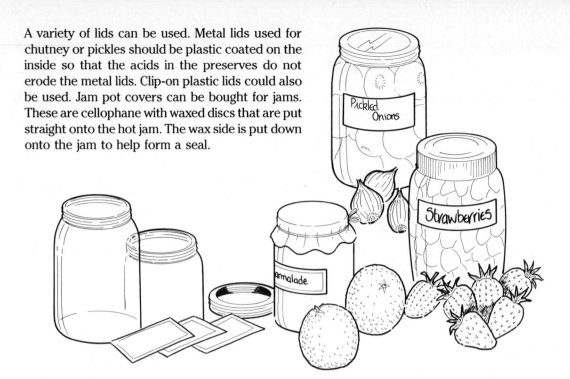

Jars, lids and labels

Polythene freezer bags should be of good quality. Different coloured bags are useful for colour coding different types of foods.

NB Always overwrap highly spiced foods or strong smelling foods in freezer bags, or heavy duty foil, otherwise such flavours will be transferred to other foods.

Freezer cling film and foil is thicker than ordinary cling film and better to use. It is ideal for covering awkward shapes.

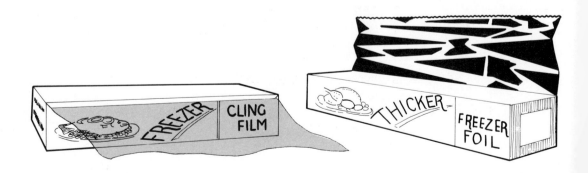

Polythene containers should be of good quality with tight fitting lids.

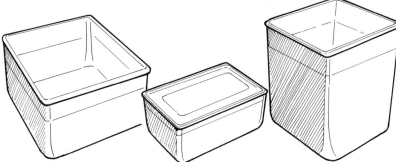

Aluminium dishes are useful for ready-cooked foods because food can be reheated in the container. The lids are not usually re-usable as they stain, but the bases can be washed and re-used.

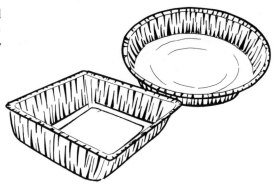

Labels should be used with the name of the product and the date clearly written on them.

Colour coding of labels can be used on freezer items.

Worksheet

Refer to Worksheets 20–4. Your teacher may divide you up into groups for experimental and practical cookery work.

You must listen to, read and follow the instructions carefully. If you are unsure of anything ask your teacher. At the end of your set task you will be reporting your findings back to the class. It is therefore important that you understand what to do.

Different methods of preservation

PRESERVING METHOD		TYPES OF FOODS	WHY IT WORKS
Use of heat	Sterilising	Milk	Above a temperature of 100 °C micro-organisms and enzymes are destroyed. Some bacteria found on vegetables are resistant to heat below 125 °C, so should not be preserved at home.
	Pasteurising	Milk, fruit, juices, beer, cream, wine	
	UHT	Milk, cream	
	Bottling	Fruit	
	Canning	Virtually all food	
Freezing		Almost all foods	Freezers operate at −18 °C. Bacteria are inactive at −10 °C. Micro-organisms are unable to grow. Enzyme action is slowed down.
		Coffee, milk, meat, vegetables, fruits	
Dehydration	Accelerated freeze drying	Meat, fruit, vegetables, herbs	Micro-organisms cannot survive without moisture. Enzymes become inactive.
Chemical	Salt	Vegetables, meat, fish	Strong solutions prevent the action of micro-organisms and enzymes.
	Vinegar	Pickles, chutney	
	Sugar	Jam, jelly making	
	Smoking	Fish, meat	
	Alcohol	Fruit	

 # Investigation

Level 1
Choose one of the home-made preserves you have already made. Compare this in taste, flavour, colour, texture and cost to its equivalent bought product. Make a chart to compare your findings.

Would you, therefore, make or buy this product and why?

Conduct a survey to find out other people's opinions. Do not let them see or hear what each other says as this could affect the results.

What conclusion did you arrive at and was the home-made product worth making?

Level 2
As you have found out from your practical work, the use of the microwave extends to making home-made preserves such as jam.

Make another preserve in the microwave and compare it with a conventional method for taste, flavour, colour, texture and cost.

What are your findings?

Books to use

Microwave recipe book provided with your microwave oven.

Family Microwave Cookery (Good Housekeeping, Ebury Press, 1985)
Good Housekeeping Complete Microwave Cookery Book (Ebury Press, 1985)

Level 3

Using the investigative procedures outlined to you on page 5, investigate the reasons for the increase in the popularity of preserved foods in the last decade.

Reading list and further sources of information:

Food preservation
Unilever Education Liason
PO Box 68, Unilever House, London EC4P 48Q

Lakeland Plastics Ltd
(Packaging for fridge, freezer and microwave)
Alexandra Buildings, Windermere, Cumbria, LA23 1BQ

Sainsbury Book of Preserves and Pickles *(Cathay Books, 1984)*
Heather Lambert

Freezer Handbook *(Ebury Press, 1980)*
Good Housekeeping

Will it Freeze Dictionary *(Home Freezer Digest, 1986)*

7 Food choices and you

All people are different, yet everyone has the same basic need from their food intake. Each individual needs a balanced diet, to include all the necessary proportions of nutrients to enable them to be healthy.

What a person eats and when a person eats depends on the individual's circumstances. We each have our own eating patterns, food preferences and methods of preparing, cooking and serving food. If you visit someone else's home it is often a surprise that their meals are different to those you have at home; this can even be true when the same or similar dishes are served.

As lifestyles change, meal patterns alter and the terms 'breakfast', 'snacks', 'lunch', 'tea' and 'supper' conjure up a variety of ideas of meals to different people, depending on their situations.

Lunch for example, could be any of these:

The school canteen

Meals on wheels for the elderly

70

A working lunch at the office

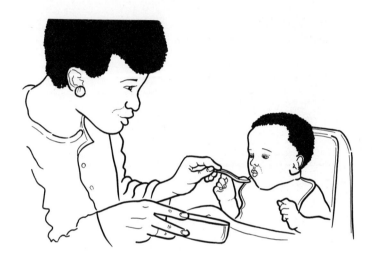

A baby starting to eat solid foods

Food choice

Food choice has become very complex, there are so many different foods to choose from. Improved technology has increased the number of commercially preserved and prepared foods available and has made food storage and cooking processes more flexible.

Gone to aerobics.
Chicken curry or
chilli con carne in
freezer, just pop
in microwave.

Love Mum X

A greater variety of imported food is also available and specialist food shops are set up to cater for the different cultures in British society.

A health food shop

A Chinese bakery in Soho

Investigation

Level 1

Look at the checklist for a healthy and interesting diet on page 74.

Use this list to find out whether pupils at your school are eating a healthy packed lunch.

Survey 20 people on the same day and record what they have to eat and drink in their packed lunches.

Record the results on a tally chart.

e.g.   Cheese sandwich   JHT III

           Fruit   JHT   (Each stroke = one person)

           Crisps   JHT JHT

Then draw this as a pictogram as shown on page 2.

Do your results show that these people eat a healthy and interesting diet? Refer to the checklist.

Level 2

Investigate the food choices available in your local community by carrying out a group survey. Visit your local shopping centre or a supermarket. Divide into smaller groups allocating each group a food section to study, e.g. fruits and vegetables, cereals including rice and pasta or dairy foods. Record the names of food available and the country of origin. This information is found on food packaging and shops often give written information about fresh foods. The groups should report back to each other and record their findings by use of a pie chart, histogram, pictogram or line graph. Refer to pages 1–8 on designing your own experiments and investigations.

Level 3

Survey the availability of specialist food shops, restaurants and take-away places within your local community. How far do these cater for the needs of a multi-cultural society?

NACNE guidelines and you

Having a greater selection of food to choose from can lead to people making unsuitable choices.

It is important that all groups of people are aware of the general guidelines to follow for a healthy and interesting diet, as well as the special needs of each group.

Checklist for a healthy and interesting diet

- Include some meat, fish or pulses each day.
- Include milk and some cheese, eggs or yoghurt each day.
- Add to this fresh vegetables and fruit.
- Do not forget the cereal foods such as rice, pasta and bread.
- Try to make colourful meals with lots of variety in flavour and texture.

The dietary groups can be organised according to age, sex and lifestyle, as discussed in Chapter 1.

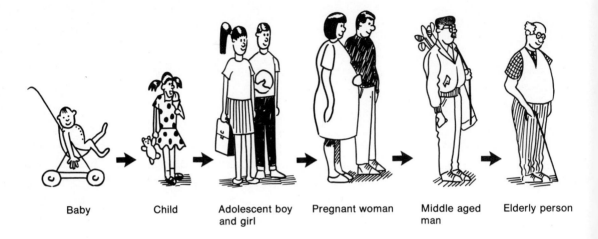

Baby   Child   Adolescent boy and girl   Pregnant woman   Middle aged man   Elderly person

Babies

Babies receive their nourishment from breast milk or formula (bottle) milk, until at about four months they are introduced to solid foods, this is known as the 'weaning' stage. There are many commercially prepared baby foods in tinned, bottled and dried form, yet it is also possible for families to mince or liquidise their own meals for the baby, providing the food is not too greasy, spicy or highly flavoured. A suitable meal would be chicken casserole, boiled potatoes and carrots, followed by fruit fool.

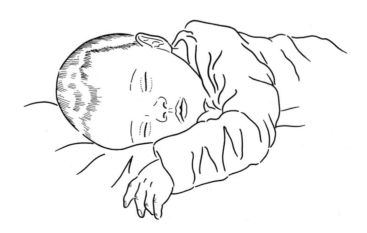

Investigation

Level 3
Compare the different varieties of baby food available with the equivalent home prepared meals for the baby. Use these headings:

Cost
Preparation time
Nutritional value (use the food labels and food tables to gain this information).

Young children

Eating patterns are established very early in childhood, therefore, it is important that young children are introduced to a variety of foods as soon as possible. Young children find greasy and spicy foods difficult to digest and should not be given peanuts as they can lodge in the throat and cause the child to choke.

Obesity
Children appreciate interesting meals that are colourful. Portions should be small as most children will ask for more if they need it. Snacks and food rewards are not a good idea in between meals: if these have a high sugar content, they may be preferred to proper meals and become a habit difficult to break. Overweight children often have great difficulty in losing weight and so a balanced diet containing protein-rich foods, particularly milk and some fresh fruit and vegetables to provide fibre, vitamins and minerals is important from the start.

Investigation

Level 3

The following guidelines are recommended for young children's diets:

- No added salt to their food.
- No added sugar to drinks, breakfast cereal and puddings.
- Use whole milk rather than skimmed milk.

Investigate the reasons for these recommendations.

Adolescence

It is at the adolescent stage that the nutritional requirements of boys and girls vary. During adolescence, physical and emotional changes occur that prepare young people's bodies for parenthood, and they become capable of reproduction. For girls this is marked by the start of menstruation (periods). During menstruation, blood is lost from the body and has to be replaced. The red pigment of blood, **haemoglobin**, contains iron, which has to be provided by eating foods rich in iron, such as liver, other red meats, pulses, bread or eggs. If insufficient iron is provided in the diet, there will be a lack of red blood cells and because these cells carry oxygen throughout the body, the person becomes tired, pale and lethargic, resulting in **anaemia**.

The energy requirements of boys in adolescence are considered to be higher than those of girls, because they are generally more active and have a lower proportion of body fat. They need filling meals and nutritious snacks, remembering that a well-balanced diet is important for good health.

Slimming and you

Young people often become aware of their images and want to look slim, attractive and healthy. Slimming diets have become very popular. Unfortunately, crash slimming diets cut out many foods that provide the body with **essential nutrients** and if they are followed, it is possible to become very ill, due to lack of nutrients.

Slimming advice

- Eat fewer energy-giving foods, such as sugars and fats.
- Eat fruit, vegetables and fibre-giving foods.
- Eat protein-rich foods.
- Eat regular meals and avoid the snacks.
- Take more exercise.

Anorexia nervosa is a phychological illness often associated with adolescent girls, although it is not restricted to this age group or sex, as young adults of both sexes are known to be sufferers. The disease is very complex and is linked to emotional problems and the person's self-image. The symptoms are, not eating or eating very little, and sometimes making themselves sick after eating. People suffering from this disease will become very thin; protein from their muscle tissue is used to provide energy, this is called 'muscle wasting'. They will also be very prone to infection as they are lacking the vitamins and mineral substances needed for good health.

Despite the fact that they are extremely thin and underweight, people suffering from anorexia nervosa picture themselves as fat and continue to starve themselves; without professional help they may die.

Pregnancy

Before birth a baby takes nourishment from the mother. Pregnant women who are poorly nourished, as in less developed countries suffering from drought and famine, may risk complications during pregnancy and their babies may be underweight at birth, born prematurely and susceptible to infections; some may even die. This situation is unlikely to occur in the UK unless the pregnant mother does not take care of herself and eat a varied diet to include the essential nutrients. Weight gain is unavoidable in pregnancy; the baby is developing, his food supply in the placenta and the fluid surrounding him all add to the weight gained. However, too many energy-giving foods should be avoided to prevent unnecessary weight gain. Sickness, indigestion and heartburn are normal, however these symptoms can be made worse by eating greasy or spicy foods. To provide the essential nourishment for herself and her baby, the mother should eat a well-balanced diet, including iron-rich foods, fibre to avoid constipation, protein-rich foods for the baby's growth and fresh fruit and vegetables to provide essential vitamins and mineral substances.

Breast-feeding

Mothers are encouraged to breast-feed their babies if possible because breast milk contains antibodies which give the baby defence against infection. Breast milk is slightly acid and contains sugar that allows harmless bacteria to grow in the baby's intestines. These in turn discourage harmful germs that produce diarrhoea and so **gastro-enteritis** is rare in breast-fed babies. Also breast milk costs nothing, it is convenient and allows the mother and baby to form a bond. It is important for breast-feeding mothers to eat well, as in pregnancy, and make sure they have a nutritionally balanced diet.

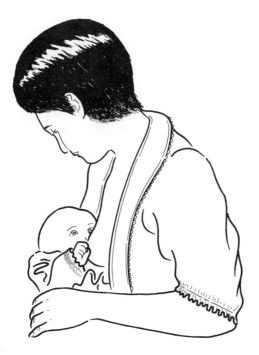

The elderly

For some elderly people their diets change very little with age. Their energy requirements may be reduced as they become less active and they may have smaller appetites, but they are still able to enjoy all the foods they are used to eating. These people should eat smaller meals but still need the same protein, vitamin and mineral intake, and so have to be more selective in their food choices. However, not all elderly people are as fortunate and many suffer from problems associated with old age.

Physical problems

- Difficulty in eating some foods because of false teeth, sore gums or indigestion.
- Difficulty in preparing some foods due to arthritis or shakiness.
- Difficulty in using some cooking methods or equipment.

Social problems

- Elderly people living alone may have lost interest in preparing and eating food.
- Elderly people managing on low incomes cannot afford to spend very much on food.

 Investigation

Level 3

Investigate the implications of the physical and social problems faced by some elderly people.

Consider how these problems may be overcome to ensure that all elderly people have a healthy diet.

Vegetarian diets

Vegetarianism seems to be becoming more popular. Certainly people are more adventurous in their choice and use of plant foods and many families regularly enjoy main meals that do not include meat or fish. There are two main types of vegetarian: a **lacto-vegetarian** and a **vegan**. A lacto-vegetarian does not eat meat, fish or any animal product produced from the slaughter of animals, e.g. lard and gelatine. A vegan eats only foods from plant sources and will not eat eggs, milk, cheese and animal fats such as butter and some margarines.

Why be a vegetarian?

Individuals choose to follow a vegetarian diet for a variety of reasons.

- They dislike the idea of animals being killed to provide humans with food.
- They dislike the taste or texture of animal flesh.
- They object to the 'wasteful' use of food when so many people in the world are starving.
- Some people feel that a vegetarian diet is more healthy.
- Some religions have laws about the foods they should not eat, e.g. some Hindus are vegetarian.
- For some, plant foods are the only foods available to them, e.g. in countries such as Ethiopia and Mozambique, where natural disasters have resulted in any crops grown being used for human consumption only.

Investigation

Level 2

How many vegetarians do you know? What are their reasons for being vegetarian? Are they lacto-vegetarians or vegans? You could extend the investigation to research the popularity of vegetarianism in your school. Find out how many vegetarian meals are provided by the school canteen each day and how many pupils have a vegetarian packed lunch.

Present your finds as a pie-chart or histogram.

Meat substitutes

Soya beans are a valuable source of protein and are used to manufacture a meat-like substance known as textured vegetable protein or TVP; this can be bought and used in place of meat in a variety of forms, e.g. mince or chunks.

'Quorn' is another meat substitute. It is a myco-protein based on a mould. It has a nutritive value similar to meat, yet it is possible to grow a good supply of this protein food in a very short time, whereas to rear animals for food production requires a large capital and time input.

Dietary guidelines for vegetarians

Lacto-vegetarians and vegans should not have any nutritional problems provided they eat a wide variety of foods from the choice available to them. Vegans have to be particularly careful to include plant protein foods such as beans, peas, lentils, nuts and cereal foods, particularly bread, in their diet. These plant proteins complement each other to provide all the essential amino acids that are present in animal protein foods, e.g. cereal protein and pulse protein complement each other in a nut roast.

Iron provided by vegetable foods is not as well absorbed by the body as iron provided by meat. Vegetarians may need to take an iron supplement to prevent anaemia. However, cereal foods containing iron and having yeast as an ingredient, do allow iron to be absorbed by the body (e.g. in bread).

The main source of vitamin B_{12} is meat and meat products, although yeast extract such as *Marmite®* is an alternative source of this vitamin. If yeast extract is not eaten regularly a tablet supplement of this vitamin is recommended.

Eating foods from each of the following food groups daily should ensure a balanced diet.

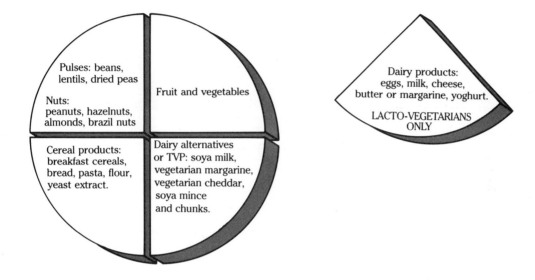

The vegetarian in the family

Not all members of a family may wish to follow a vegetarian diet. This can cause difficulties or added work in food buying, meal planning and food preparation for the family.

Worksheet

Now look at Worksheet 25 on feeding the family, and complete it.

 # Investigation

Level 1

Investigate ways in which dishes may be adapted to cater for the lacto-vegetarian in the family.

Use the following method.

1   Make a checklist of foods eaten or not eaten by the lacto-vegetarian, e.g.

FOODS EATEN	FOODS NOT EATEN

2   By asking members of your class, make a list of popular dishes eaten by families.

3   Using a highlighter pen or felt pen, pick out those dishes that are not suitable for the lacto-vegetarian.

4   Using a highlighter pen or felt pen, pick out those dishes that are not suitable for the lacto-vegetarian.

Meat dish
Spaghetti bolognese
200 g minced beef
1 onion
1 clove garlic
Tin tomatoes
1 tablespoon tomato puree
1 beef stock cube
150 ml water
Spaghetti

Adapted lacto-vegetarian dish
Vegetable bolognese
50 g mushrooms
½ green pepper
1 stick celery
1 onion
1 clove garlic
Tin tomatoes
1 tablespoon tomato puree
150 ml water
Spaghetti
To Serve: Top with 50 g grated cheese

5   Record your findings by making your own lacto-vegetarian recipe leaflet.

6   Were there any recipes you could not adapt? What were these? What different dishes could you choose instead?

Reading list and further sources of information:

Health Education Council
(leaflets and video tapes on healthy diets for children, pregnant women and the elderly)
78 New Oxford Street, London WC1A 1AH

Help the Aged
16–18 St James's Walk, London EC1R 0BE

Video
You Never Grow Old At The Table
(nutrition for the senior citizen)
British Gas Education Service,
PO Box 46, Hounslow, Middlesex, TW4 6NF.

The Vegetarian Society
53 Marloes Road, Kensington, London W8 6LA

The Vegan Society
47 Highlands Road, Leatherhead, Surrey

Anorexic Aid
11 Priory Centre, High Wycombe, Bucks.

The Consumers' Association
14 Buckingham Street, London WC2N 6DS

Not Just a Load of Old Lentils *(Fontana/Collins, 1984)*
Rose Elliot

Eastern Vegetarian Cookery *(Jonathan Cape, 1983)*
Madhur Jaffrey

Sarah Brown's Vegetarian Cookbook *(Dorling Kindersley, 1986)*

The Taste of Health (BBC Guide to Healthy Eating) *(BBC, 1985)*

Raw Energy *(Century Arrow, 1986)*
Leslie and Susannah Kenton

8 Equipment, technology and ergonomics

The lifestyles of individuals and the number of people within a family will affect the choice and use of equipment in the home. For example, many women have employment outside the home and individual family members have more independence and may follow their own leisure activities and other interests that draw them away from the home. Therefore, less time is spent on food preparation, cooking and washing-up, washing clothes and cleaning the house and 'high-tech' equipment for the home has become more popular. As a result, the standard of living of many people has improved.

High-tech equipment for the home can include a fully automatic washing machine, a tumble drier, a freezer, a dishwasher, a food processor and a microwave oven.

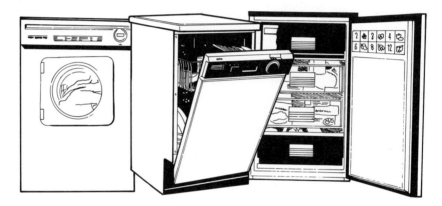

Kitchens also have to meet the needs of the family and the size, layout and equipment of the kitchen will vary according to the number of people, their ages, occupations and lifestyles.

Equipment for the home is becoming increasingly sophisticated. Designers and manufacturers are aware of the consumers' need for time and labour-saving equipment to cope with regular tasks. They also need to ensure that the equipment is safe to use, relatively economical to buy and run and is aesthetically designed. This can be seen when considering new developments in equipment design, for example, the halogen hob gives a similar instant heat to that provided by gas when cooking. The recently developed induction hob works by heating only the metal base of the saucepan, preventing the waste of heat energy and also making the hob safe to touch. Electric kettle designs have changed; the traditional shape has been replaced by the taller jug model, which has a smaller base and element, allowing the user to heat as little as one cup of water and so save energy.

Other developments are concerned with the safety of the environment. For example, refrigerators and freezers are being developed with CFC-free coolant systems. This is an important issue as Chlorofluorocarbons (CFCs) are responsible for trapping heat in the earth's atmosphere and CFC11 and CFC12 cause thinning of the ozone layer and allow holes to form. Some scientists believe this could have a dramatic effect on our climate. Some types of foam insulated packaging, such as those used to hold take-away foods and those used as trays for meat and other fresh products also release harmful CFCs into the atmosphere and economical replacements are being sought by manufacturers.

Investigation

Level 2
Investigate the design features of one of these products:

A cool wall, variable slot toaster
An automatic washer drier
A 12 place-setting dishwasher
A microwave combination oven

Evaluate the item with reference to these points;
Safety
Economy
Efficiency

Saucepans are indispensible items of kitchen equipment. They can be made from a variety of materials as well as combinations of materials. It is now believed that aluminium saucepans can cause damage to brain cells and the use of them should therefore be avoided.

Worksheet

Carry out the survey on Worksheet 26 on the purpose of packaging.

Investigation

Level 2
Investigate the best saucepan for a particular function, e.g. boiling milk. Select a number of saucepans each made from a different material. Carry out an experiment to test the suitability of each saucepan to the task. Record your results under the following headings:

Time taken to boil
Heat of handle
Ease of cleaning
Ease of pouring

Evaluate your results.

Kitchen ergonomics

Kitchens are work centres and careful planning is needed so that the work can be carried out easily and efficiently. There has been a lot of research into the ways people carry out tasks such as preparing food, cooking food and clearing up afterwards. Researchers found that these jobs take place around three centres of activity:

- The food storage areas (e.g. fridge, freezer, cupboards);
- The preparation and cleaning up areas (the sink, work surfaces);
- The cooking areas (e.g. oven, grill, hotplate, microwave oven, electric kettle).

The distance between these areas make up the three sides of the 'work triangle'.

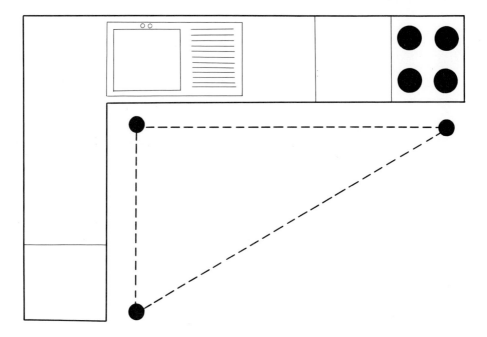

In an efficient kitchen, the total distance of the three sides of the triangle should be less than 6.6 metres.

 Investigation

Level 1
Carry out your own experiment to prove the work triangle theory. Work with a partner. One partner completes a simple task, e.g. making a cup of coffee, including clearing away or making a simple toasted snack and clearing away.

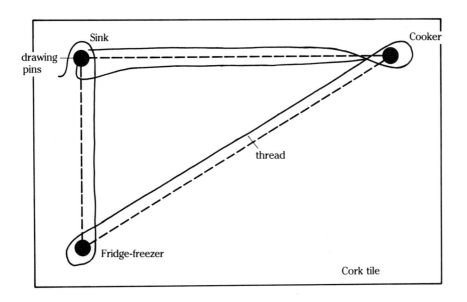

The other partner observes the process and follows the movement between the three work areas by plotting it with thread on a cork board or tile. If you want to be very accurate, the drawing pins could be positioned to scale to represent the actual work triangle. At the end of the task the thread could be measured and the actual distance covered could be calculated. Kitchens vary in size and shape, but there are a number of basic layouts to consider. Look at the position of the working triangle in the following examples.

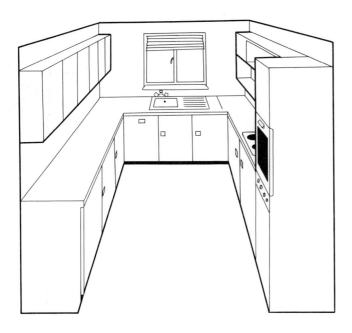

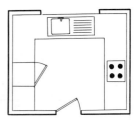

The 'U' shaped kitchen

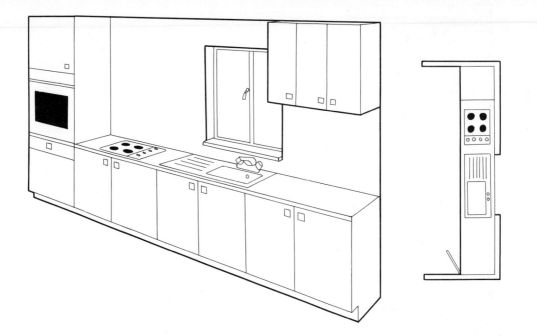

The galley kitchen

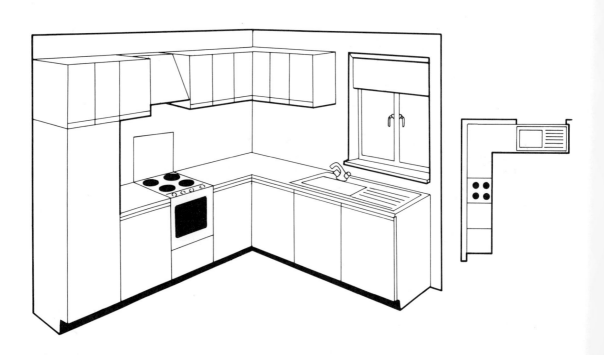

The 'L' shaped kitchen

88

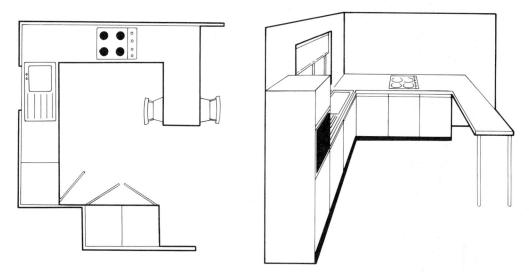

The peninsula design

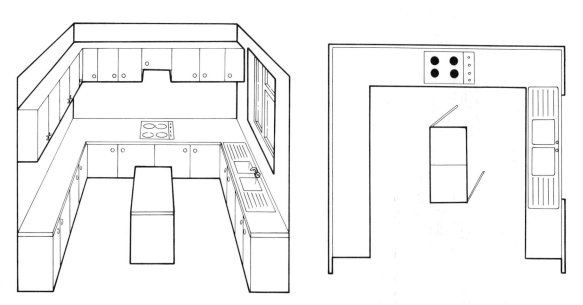

The island design

The peninsula and island designs are popular for large kitchens. Look for different kitchen designs in magazines and kitchen showrooms.

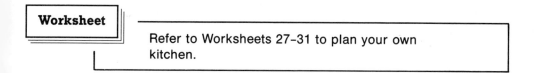

Worksheet

Refer to Worksheets 27–31 to plan your own kitchen.

Choosing equipment

Choosing equipment for the tasks to be carried out in the home depends on understanding the individual needs of the family.

 # Investigation

Level 1
Carry out these experiments and consider the use of the food processor and the microwave oven for different households, e.g. a person living alone, a family with children, where friends are frequently dropping in at mealtimes, or a household with an elderly person or physically disabled person who does a share of the food preparation.

Coleslaw in yoghurt dressing

You will need
¼ white cabbage
2 sticks celery
1 apple, and 2 teaspoons lemon juice
½ small onion
25 g sultanas or raisins
25 g peanuts
1 tablespoon parsley (optional)
125 ml natural yoghurt

What to do
1 *Shred the cabbage finely.*

2 *Slice the celery thinly.*

3 *Core and dice the apple (leave the skin to increase the fibre content, sprinkle with lemon juice to prevent browning).*

4 *Peel and finely dice the onion.*

5 *Chop the parsley.*

6 *Put all the ingredients into a mixing bowl and mix until coated in the yoghurt dressing.*

Group 1
Make coleslaw following the recipe given above, use the equipment listed below as appropriate:

French cook's knife
vegetable knife
cheese grater.

Group 2

Make coleslaw following the recipe, use the food processor as appropriate, refer to the instruction booklet if you are unsure how to use it.

Use the shredding blade for the white cabbage.

Use the slicing blade for the celery and apple (remove the core before processing).

Use the metal blade to dice the onion.

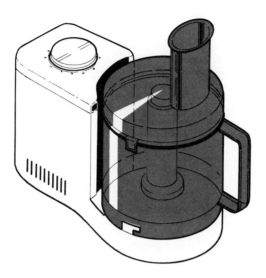

Both Groups

Compare the results for each ingredient with the other group.

Record all results as shown below:

FOOD ITEM	METHOD PREP.	PREP. TIME	APPEARANCE	TEXTURE

What conclusions can you draw from this experiment?

Which method gave the best results?

Which group had the most washing up and clearing away?

When would a food processor be most useful for making coleslaw?

Investigate the other uses of the food processor (use the instruction booklet and recipe books).

Find out the prices of different makes and models of food processors.

Evaluate your work.

Investigation

Level 1
Investigate different ways of cooking white and brown long-grain rice.

Rice salad

You will need
200 g rice
¼ teaspoon salt
2 spring onions
1 red pepper
50 g raisins
2 tablespoons parsley (optional)
2 tablespoons soy sauce
½ tablespoon sunflower oil

What to do
1   *Cook the rice according to the instructions on the packet.*

2   *Wash and finely slice the spring onions.*

3   *Wash, core, de-seed and dice the red pepper.*

4   *Wash and chop the parsley.*

5   *Put all the ingredients except the oil and soy sauce into a mixing bowl.*

6   *Mix the oil and soy sauce together and coat the other ingredients with this dressing.*

Group 1
Use white long-grain rice.

Group 2
Use brown long-grain rice.

Cook 100 g rice according to the instructions on the packet.

Cook 100 g rice in the microwave oven, using the cooking guide in your microwave oven handbook.

Write out the methods used for cooking the rice.

Record the results of both groups, as shown below:

RICE	COOKING PROCESS	COOKING TIME	APPEARANCE	TASTE	TEXTURE